BRAIN GAMES FOR BRAIN POWER

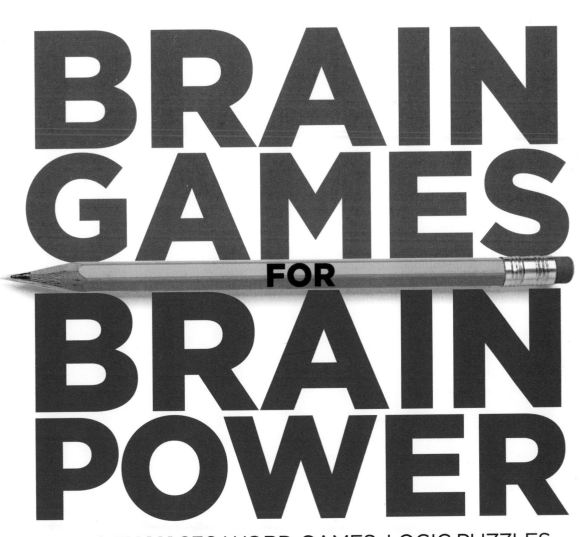

MORE THAN 250 WORD GAMES, LOGIC PUZZLES, NUMBER CHALLENGES, AND TRIVIA QUIZZES

TRUSTED MEDIA BRANDS

New York / Montreal

Printed in China
10 9 8 7 6 5 4 3 2 1

Note to Readers
The consultants, writers, editors, and proofreaders have taken all reasonable measures to confirm and verify the accuracy of the information contained in this title. However, some statements of fact can be open to interpretation. Similarly, new information and research often reveal that long-held beliefs are not true. We welcome your input on any answers for which you have sound evidence may be incorrect.

STAY SHARP, STAY YOUNG

The puzzles in this book may help you improve a variety of brain skills, including your ability to remember. As the brain ages, vocabulary may remain strong, but the ability to spot meanings and search for the word you are looking for slows down.

Language puzzles exercise circuits that can help lessen forgetful moments and shorten their duration, but learning cannot become memory without concentration, and without regular maintenance, concentration shrinks with age. These puzzles provide many opportunities for improving and strengthening this important ability and many other useful brain skills:

- pattern and pathfinding puzzles will strengthen your powers of concentration in the same way that physical exercises build aerobic stamina;

- logic and memory puzzles will challenge your working memory because you must keep some variables in mind while you test them against others—this frontal-lobe skill is crucial to productive thinking and requires fierce concentration;

- visual and mechanical puzzles will stretch your visual-spatial mental muscles, which you need to navigate the physical world successfully;

- divergent thinking puzzles will encourage your ability to think "outside the box" and see links where others see standard differences—an ability that pays off in any profession;

- puzzles involving calculation are important to try—even if you are not a numbers person—for they light up many different parts of the brain at once.

Descriptions of the major puzzle types appear on the following pages. The puzzles and games start on page 8. Good luck!

About the Puzzles

Brain Games for Brain Power is filled with a delightful mix of classic and new puzzle types. To help you get started, here are instructions, tips, and some examples.

WORD GAMES

CROSSWORD PUZZLES

Clues are the deciding factor that determines crossword-solving difficulty. Many solvers mistakenly think strange and unusual words are what make a puzzle challenging. In reality, crossword constructors generally try to avoid grid esoterica, opting for familiar words and expressions.

WORD SEARCHES

In a word search, the challenge is to find hidden words within a grid of letters. Words can be found in vertical columns or horizontal rows or along diagonals, with the letters of the words running either forward or backward.

WORD SUDOKU

The basic sudoku puzzle is a 9 x 9 square grid, split into nine square regions, each containing nine cells. You need to complete the grid so that each row, each column, and each 3 x 3 frame contains the nine letters from the black box above the grid.

There is always a hidden nine-letter word in the diagonal from top left to bottom right.

EXAMPLE　　　　**SOLUTION**

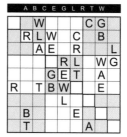

WORD POWER

These quizzes test your knowledge of grammar and language and help you develop a better vocabulary. Find out where you stand on the Word Power scale by using the simple rating system included on the answer pages.

NUMBER GAMES

SUDOKU

The basic sudoku puzzle is a 9 x 9 square grid, split into nine square regions, each containing nine cells. Complete the grid so that each row, each column and each 3 x 3 frame contains every number from 1 to 9.

EXAMPLE

		2	1		5			
	3		2					
8				3				
	1					8		
6		9					4	2
4	7						5	9
1	8	6	4					
5			3	8			7	6
	9		5		6	4		8

SOLUTION

7	4	2	1	6	5	8	9	3
9	3	5	2	4	8	7	6	1
8	6	1	7	3	9	5	2	4
2	1	3	9	5	4	6	8	7
6	5	9	8	7	3	1	4	2
4	7	8	6	1	2	3	5	9
1	8	6	4	9	7	2	3	5
5	2	4	3	8	1	9	7	6
3	9	7	5	2	6	4	1	8

In addition to classic sudoku puzzles, you'll find **SUDOKU X** puzzles, where the main diagonals must include every number from 1 to 9, and **SUDOKU TWINS** with two overlapping grids.

KAKURO

These puzzles are like crosswords with numbers. There are clues across and down, but the clues are numbers. The solution is a sum which adds up to the clue number.

Each number in a black area is the sum of the numbers that you have to enter in the next empty boxes. The empty boxes that make up the sum are called a run. The sum of the across run is written above the diagonal in the black area, while the sum of the down run is written below the diagonal.

Runs can contain only the numbers 1 through 9, and each number in a run can be used only once. The gray boxes contain only odd numbers and the white, only even numbers.

EXAMPLE   **SOLUTION**

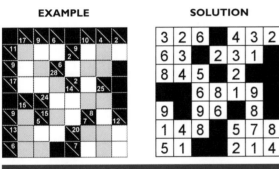

LOGIC PUZZLES

BINAIRO

Binairo puzzles look similar to sudoku puzzles. They are just as simple and challenging, but that is where the similarity ends.

There are two versions: odd and even. The even puzzles feature a 12 x 12 grid. You need to complete the grid with zeros and ones, until there are 6 zeros and 6 ones in every row and every column. No more than two of the same number can be next to or under each other. Rows or columns with exactly the same combination are not allowed.

EXAMPLE   **SOLUTION**

The odd puzzles feature an 11 x 11 grid. You need to complete the grid with zeros and ones until there are 5 zeros and 6 ones in every row and column.

KEEP GOING

In this puzzle, start on a blank square of your choice and connect as many blank squares as possible with one single continuous line.

You can only connect squares along vertical and horizontal lines, not along diagonals. You must continue the connecting line up until the next obstacle—i.e., the rim of the box, a black square, or a square that has already been used.

You can change direction at any obstacle you meet. Each square can be used only once. The number of blank squares left unused is marked in the upper square. There may be more than one solution, but we include only one solution in our answer key.

EXAMPLE   **SOLUTION**

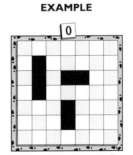
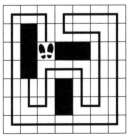

About the Puzzles (continued)

NUMBER CLUSTER

Number cluster puzzles are language-free, logical numerical problems. They consist of cubes on a 6 x 6 grid. Numbers have been placed in some of the cubes, while the rest are empty. Your challenge is to complete the grid by creating runs of the same number and length as the number supplied. So, where a cube with the number 5 has been included on the grid, you need to create a run of five number 5's, including the cube already shown. The run can be horizontal, vertical, or both horizontal and vertical.

WORD PYRAMID

Each word in the pyramid has the letters of the word above it, plus a new letter.

Using the clues given, answer No. 1 and then work your way to the base of the pyramid to complete the word pyramid.

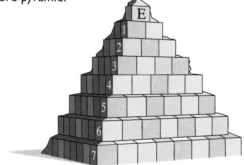

SPORT MAZE

This puzzle is presented on a 6 x 6 grid. Your starting point is indicated by a red cell with a ball and a number. Your objective is to draw the shortest route from the ball to the goal, the only square without a number. You can move only along vertical and horizontal lines, but not along diagonals. The figure on each square indicates the number of squares the ball must be moved in the same direction. You can change direction at each stop.

CAGE THE ANIMALS

This puzzle presents you with a zoo divided into a 16 x 16 grid. The different animals on the grid need to be separated. Draw lines that will completely divide up the grid into smaller squares, with exactly one animal per square.

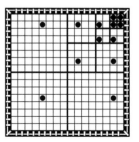

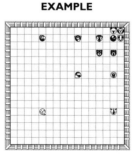

TRIVIA

TRIVIA QUIZZES & TRIVIAL PURSUITS

Trivia in a variety of formats and topics will probe the depth of your knowledge of facts. Questions and answers will tempt, tease, and tickle.

VISUAL PUZZLES

Throughout you will find unique mazes, visual conundrums, and other colorful challenges. Each comes with a new name and unique instructions. Our best advice? Patience and perseverance. Your eyes will need time to unravel the visual secrets.

BRAINSNACK® PUZZLES

To solve a BrainSnack® puzzle, you must think logically. You'll need to use one or several strategies to detect direction, differences, and/or similarities, associations, calculations, order, spatial insight, colors, quantities, and distances. A BrainSnack® ensures that all the brain's capacities are fully engaged. These are brain sports at their best!

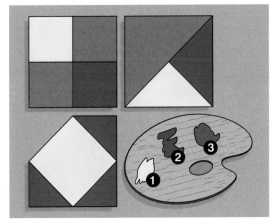

WEATHER CHARTS

We all want to know the weather forecast, and here's your chance to figure it out! Arrows are scattered on a grid. Each arrow points toward a space where a weather symbol should be, but the symbols cannot be next to each other vertically, horizontally, or diagonally. A symbol cannot be placed on top of an arrow. You must determine where the symbols should be placed.

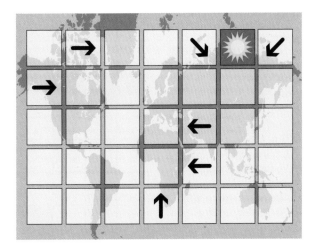

BRAINTEASERS

You'll also find short brainteasers scattered throughout these pages. These puzzles will give you a little light relief from the more intense puzzles while still challenging you.

CROSSWORD

Baker's Bliss

ACROSS

1 Kitchen tool for beating an egg
6 Stomach muscles, for short
9 Auto additive initials
12 Baseball great Hank
13 Fish eggs
14 Green veggie
15 Serious TV show
16 ___ pin, baking tool
18 Eden inhabitant
20 Untrue
21 Prep an oven
25 Leaves the engine running
26 Prefix before *dynamic* or *nautical*
27 Fill
29 Erupt like a volcano
30 Green federal agency (abbrev.)
31 Punta ___, Dominican Republic
35 Type of chowder
36 Work safety agency (abbrev.)
37 St Pat's month
41 Kitchen implement for scraping
43 Nebraska city
44 Ctrl + ___ + del
45 ___ extract, baking ingredient
48 Temporary failure
52 At my wit's ___
53 Family
54 Incite (2 words)
55 Author Bradbury
56 Hankering
57 Ingredient to make baked goods rise

DOWN

1 Lump
2 Laughter syllable
3 Certain savings account (abbrev.)
4 For a reason not known
5 Scoundrel
6 At the airport, opposite of DEP (abbrev.)
7 Halloween greeting
8 Photo of the photographer
9 Splatter a liquid
10 Stressed out
11 *War and Peace* has more than 1,400
17 Young boy
19 Painter's stand
21 ___ *de deux*
22 Spokesperson (abbrev.)
23 Before, poetically
24 Spanish appetizers
28 Florida city
31 Kind of cheese
32 Home of the Sun Devils
33 U.S. and Canadian sports group (abbrev.)
34 Travel group (abbrev.)
35 Pale
37 Shaker's partner
38 Iowa's ___ Colonies
39 Country singer Travis
40 The Windy City, for short
42 Type of cat
46 Fib
47 *CW* traveling editor Kaiser
49 Jack Nicklaus' and Arnold Palmer's group (abbrev.)
50 Call for help
51 Otolaryngologist's specialty (abbrev.)

Cage the Animals

Draw lines to completely divide up the grid into small squares with exactly one animal per square. The squares should not overlap.

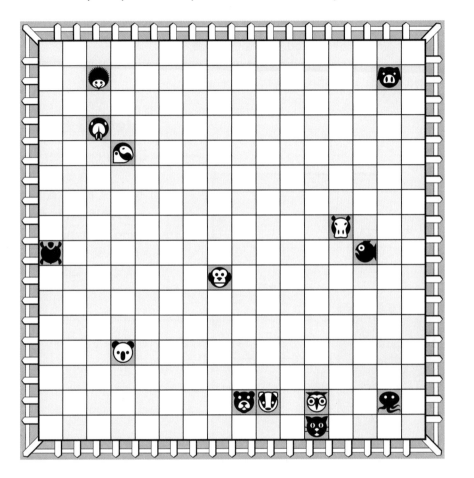

do you KNOW?

Which weapon of war was first used in 1916?

_____

_____

LETTERBLOCKS

Move the letterblocks around so that words are formed on top and below that are associated with clothes.

T	C	*	O	N	O	T
T	L	R	E	E	H	A

Keep Going

Start on a blank square of your choice and connect as many blank squares as possible with one single continuous line. You can only connect squares along vertical and horizontal lines, not along diagonal lines. You must continue the connecting line up until the next obstacle, i.e., the rim of the box, a black square or a square that has already been used. You can change direction at any obstacle you meet. Each square can only be used once. The number of blank squares that will be left unused is marked in the upper square. There is more than one solution. We only show one solution.

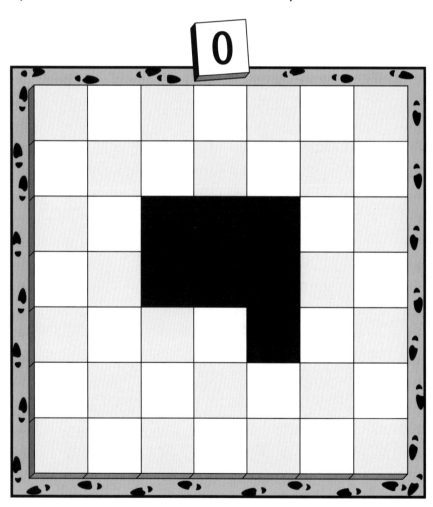

delete ONE

Delete one letter from

SHE'S NOT A PARISIAN

and rearrange the rest to find another lady.

CROSSWORD **Winners**

ACROSS

1 Pear variety
5 Disrobe
10 Cognizant of
14 On ___ with (equal)
15 End of a bookie's quote
16 Gather grain
17 2011 Belmont winner
19 Champ's wear
20 Fred in *Easter Parade*
21 Covered passageways
23 *2001* and *2010* studio
24 Like Victorian collars
25 Abhor
29 Approaches
32 Charlton Heston film
33 Smelting refuse
35 Suffix for press
36 Tylenol target
37 Blood carriers
38 Chew a bone
39 Principle
40 *Simon Boccanegra* setting
41 Bankrupt
42 Baseball card collectors, at times
44 Attached, in a way
46 Sublet
47 Arctic explorer John
48 Marsh plant
51 Big bills
55 "Purple ___": Hendrix
56 2011 Oscar-winning actor
58 "Rock of ___"
59 No honor ___ thieves
60 Western alliance
61 Bombard
62 Minor error
63 Pesky insect

DOWN

1 Theda of the silents
2 *Bloom County* character
3 2010 Angelina Jolie film
4 Three Stooges prop
5 Enya's "___ in Africa"
6 Phone sound
7 Hugh Capet, e.g.
8 Pre-Columbian empire
9 Unequaled
10 Jerry of *Law & Order*
11 2011 Grammy-winning song
12 *A Bronx ___* (1993)
13 Acts on a preference
18 Boardlike
22 Old Deuteronomy's musical
25 Apportioned
26 *MacGyver* star Dana
27 2011 Masters winner
28 "Lest we lose our ___": Browning
29 Freeman and Lisa
30 Duckling's dad
31 Stitched
34 Carioca's city
37 Like some blinds
38 Card type
40 Nolin of *Baywatch*
41 Zach in *Garden State*
43 Abhor
45 Quail
48 Bloke
49 Danish opera singer Haugland
50 Texas mesa
51 Scuba gear
52 Esfahan locale
53 Wonder Woman's friend
54 Beyond repair
57 Cut off

Comfort Foods

All the words are hidden vertically, horizontally or diagonally—
in both directions.

```
U K F H E S E E H C D E L L I R G L O
I F L R F Y F Y L K X T S A O R T O P
K G R I T S Q S P O P C O R N N L T J
A O C O C M J W T L R J E Y A E E K P
T Z I V L O E B W U J E M D A K Q J M
Z J X Y X T E I R E N A S D L C A A W
R C L X S D N T I O J O E S C I S P C
T J I W S G C P X T W S D S A H L T Z
B L Q N S P E O S S E N B O E C D F M
M F V U N L A G O E T I I D Q D G I M
N I G X P A N G H K R Z P E R E R K E
X V T P B I M C H Y I O U G S I E A A
C U A Z L R D O E E T E O K G R B M T
K J K P U N A J N A T A S C T F M H L
U H M Q A V O O T R D T Z S J V J Y O
O U Q C T D Q O S P O R I Z L X V T A
D P A D C J E U J T N L W G I A V D F
W M L F M S D Z P F M X L B V P H L D
B U R G E R S H V J A N G A S A L B U
```

- APPLE PIE
- BROWNIES
- BURGERS
- CASSEROLE
- CINNAMON ROLL
- COCOA
- COOKIES
- DONUTS
- DUMPLINGS
- FRIED CHICKEN
- GRILLED CHEESE
- GRITS
- LASAGNA
- MAC AND CHEESE
- MASHED POTATOES
- MEAT LOAF
- PIZZA
- POPCORN
- POT ROAST
- RIBS
- SOUP
- SPAGHETTI
- STEW
- WINGS

Sport Maze

Draw the shortest way from the ball to the goal. You can only move along vertical and horizontal lines, not along diagonal lines. The figure on each square indicates the number of squares the ball must be moved in the same direction. You can change direction at each stop.

5	5	3	5	5	1
5	1	4	2	2	2
1	2	●	0	4	3
3	2	2	0	4	5
4	3	3	1	3	1
1	3	2	1	5	3

change ONE

Change one letter in each of these two words to form a common two-word phrase.

FREAK GOWN

ONE LETTER LESS OR MORE

The word on the right side contains the letters of the word on the left side plus or minus the letter in the middle. One letter is already in the right place.

Peanuts #1

ACROSS

1 Burlap fiber
5 Lower oneself
10 Ablutionary vessel
14 Clarinet cousin
15 Brass button?
16 ___-Rooter
17 *Charlotte's Web* girl
18 Walter ___ Disney
19 *La Dolce Vita* composer
20 Thoughtful *Peanuts* character
22 Wholesaler
24 *Gone With the Wind* locale
25 Encounters
26 Born as
27 Literally
30 *The Last Remake of Beau ___* (1977)
33 Pyongyang locale
34 "Either he goes ___ go!"
35 Tolkien cannibals
36 Assemble
37 Adjective suffix
38 Kyrgyzstan city
39 Dancer Cunningham
40 Popped the question
41 Convince
43 Spanish gold
44 Drying kilns
45 Almond candy
49 It's for the birds
51 Snoopy's WWI foe
52 Foxx in *Sanford and Son*
53 Grenoble's river
55 "I ___ you so!"
56 City on the Oka River
57 Crab claw
58 German duck
59 "Don't stop"
60 Studio stand
61 Recolored

DOWN

1 Teamsters president
2 Thumbs-up critic
3 Principled
4 Flags
5 Alluringly slender
6 *Rocky* actress Shire
7 *Alias* Emmy winner Lena
8 Eggs
9 Annoyed
10 List of mistakes
11 Snoopy's secretary
12 Major ending
13 Laugh loudly
21 "... with a banjo on my ___"
23 "And Still" singer McEntire
25 "Natural High" singer Haggard
27 Kind of mail
28 *Dies* ___ (Latin hymn)
29 Not spicy
30 Gunk
31 Gaelic
32 *Peanuts* pianist
33 Turkish natives
36 Dante's love
37 All alone
39 Terpsichore, for one
40 "Ahab the ___"
42 Kind of soap or shoe
43 Trying time
45 Hostess Mesta
46 *Gulliver's Travels* feature
47 Nick in *48 Hrs.*
48 Over and done
49 Shoot ___ the hip
50 Eliel Saarinen's son
51 *Cheers* actor Roger
54 "Get a Job" song syllable

Spot the Differences

Find the nine differences between the two images.

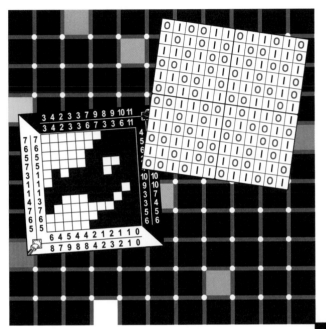

do you KNOW?

What is the only
even prime
number?

_____

_____

trivia

- Which mammal is the swiftest runner
  over short distances?

_____

Word Pyramid

Each word in the pyramid has the letters of the word above it, plus a new letter.

E
(1) compass point
(2) group of things
(3) animal refuge
(4) small picture inserted within the bounds of a larger one
(5) game
(6) vivid
(7) German physicist who
    formulated the theory of relativity

do you KNOW

What sort of
creature is a
bustard?

CROSSWORD Endless

ACROSS

1 Concerning
5 Joanna Lumley sitcom
10 Made the event
14 Theodore Cleaver's nickname
15 "Don't ___ me!"
16 Seaweed gelatin
17 Victoria or George, e.g.
18 Do a bang-up job?
19 Rocky crags
20 Ageless love conflict
23 ___-disant (so-called)
24 Routing word
25 "x + y = z" subject
29 Kettledrums
33 New hand
34 Mia in *Legend*
36 *A Question of Blood* author Rankin
37 Gloria Estefan hit
41 *Andy Capp* cartoonist Smythe
42 French tennis star Monfils
43 OPEC vessel
44 Alert and suspicious
47 Political liberal
49 ___ Anne de Beaupré
50 *Blue Hawaii* neckwear
51 #1 hit for Paula Abdul
60 Shakespearean royal
61 "___ the Song": Gladys Knight
62 Friend of François
63 Cross letters
64 Like Jiminy Glick
65 Submissive
66 Two-___ sloth
67 "Darn!"
68 *First Wives Club* members

DOWN

1 Competent
2 Bucket ___
3 *I'll ___ You There* (Oates novel)
4 Boss
5 Aquila's bright star
6 A micro sci.
7 *Star Wars* character Boba ___
8 Salieri opera
9 La Paz citizen
10 40 winks
11 Open-mouthed
12 Clayey fertilizer
13 Killarney language
21 Prize awarded Mother Teresa
22 Goal
25 "Billy, Don't Be ___" (1974 hit)
26 Add pep to (with "up")
27 Shorthand inventor
28 Syrian president (1971–2000)
29 Vibrating sound
30 Garlic mayonnaise
31 Altar approaches
32 Like helium
35 Scarfed down
38 Accepts
39 Messenger boy
40 Sue
45 Log-on name
46 4-wheel drive transport
48 Baffles
51 Act the butterfly
52 Wine combiner
53 Like Lowell's June day
54 After-bath wear
55 Belgian river
56 Tobacco kiln
57 Giant-screen theater
58 Frost coating
59 Cask dregs

MIND MAZE # Lost in Squares

Can you find your way to the middle of the mystical maze below, starting at the arrow?
Give yourself 5 minutes to complete the puzzle.

Sudoku

Fill in the grid so that each row, each column and each 3 x 3 frame contains every number from 1 to 9.

4				8	7			
	8	7	3	4			9	2
						4		7
		3		2				
	1	5				2	7	
				6		5		
2		9						
8	5			7	3	6	4	
			5	9				1

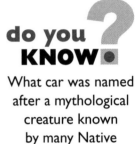

do you KNOW

What car was named after a mythological creature known by many Native Americans.

_____

_____

Pet Dogs

ACROSS

1 Bones of Sleepy Hollow
5 *My Fair Lady* horse race
10 Catch sight of
14 Sitarist Shankar
15 Joe in *Apollo 13*
16 "Elite Eight" org.
17 Where Adam met Eve
18 Something to stake
19 ___ de France
20 Doc Brown's dog
22 "Over the Rainbow" composer Arlen
24 Remote
25 He spied on Joshua
26 Henrietta, N.Y. campus
27 Transported
30 "Ship of the desert"
33 *Baywatch Hawaii* actress Eleniak
34 Dr. of rap
35 "I've Got ___ in Kalamazoo"
36 Airs
37 Arable soil
38 Capek robot play
39 Ebb and others
40 *Memoirs of a Geisha* setting
41 Didn't go
43 "Age cannot wither ___ ..."
44 *Damn Yankees* composer
45 Twelfth graders
49 "Jacob's ___": Huey Lewis
51 Doc's dog on *Fraggle Rock*
52 12th Hebrew month
53 Wake-up call
55 "___ Rock": Simon & Garfunkel
56 Sneaker brand
57 "Walk ___ Man": 4 Seasons
58 Shadowbox
59 Pippin
60 "Card Players Quarreling" artist
61 Frost hair

DOWN

1 AKC category
2 Diameter halves
3 *Mystic Pizza* props
4 Jongleur
5 Gradient
6 Bowling "lily"
7 Scott of *Hawaii Five-O*
8 "Don't Blame It ___" (Congos reggae tune)
9 Woody's voice in *Toy Story*
10 Access
11 Shaggy's Great Dane
12 Giamatti in *John Adams*
13 Summer sale site
21 Kite stabilizer
23 Thomas ___ Edison
25 Loonies, e.g.
27 Apollo in *Rocky 2*
28 He was, in Latin 101
29 Floor model
30 Ex-NBA player "Big Dog"
31 A fit of shivering
32 Winslow family's Great Dane
33 Where to get down from
36 Necessary nutrients
37 Johnny Mercer, for one
39 10-point Q, e.g.
40 Casino game
42 All mixed up
43 One of the Munsters
45 "Shop 'til you drop" trip
46 1900 zoological discovery
47 Hire a new crew
48 Square one
49 Shoot a film
50 "And every third word ___ ...": Shak.
51 Rice wine
54 Aflame

BRAINSNACK® Balance the Scales

How many blue balls have to replace the question mark in scale D so that it is in balance just like the other scales?

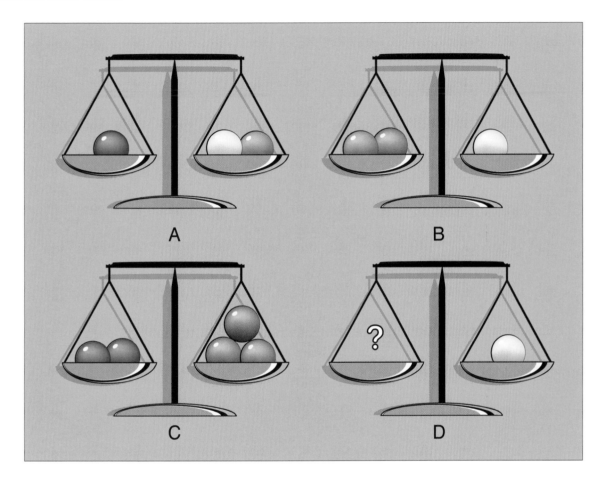

ONE LETTER LESS OR MORE

The word on the right side contains the letters of the word on the left side plus or minus the letter in the middle. One letter is already in the right place

A T L A N T I C -N ☐ ☐ ☐ T ☐ ☐

Binairo

Complete the grid with zeros and ones until there are 5 zeros and 6 ones in every row and every column. No more than two of the same number can be next to or under each other. Rows or columns with exactly the same content are not allowed. There is only one valid solution.

1						1		0		
			1							
				0			0			
	0		0					0		
		1			1		0			
							1	1		
			0		1					
1		0				1		0		
	0	0		1				1		
			1				1			

REPOSITION PREPOSITION

Unscramble **EXCERPT OF** and find a two-word preposition.

_____

22

23

WORD POWER Did I Get That Right?

Do you ever toss off an impressive-sounding word at a
cocktail party only to wonder: Did I get that right?
The terms in this quiz, inspired by the book *You're Saying It Wrong*
by Ross and Kathryn Petras, will make you sound like the smartest
person in the room—if your pronusrect.

. . . .

1. detritus *n.*—A: subtracted amount. B: debris. C: falsified claim.

2. prerogative *n.*—A: educated guess. B: first choice. C: special right.

3. segue *v.*—A: transition. B: completely surround. C: begin a court case.

4. hegemony *n.*—A: domination. B: smooth blend. C: large family.

5. dais *n.*—A: group leader. B: garden fountain. C: raised platform.

6. kefir *n.*—A: verbal skirmish. B: fermented milk. C: painting technique.

7. peremptory *adj.*—A: allowing no disagreement. B: coming first. C: walking quickly.

8. quay *n.*—A: wharf. B: small island. C: dram of brandy.

9. machination *n.*—A: study of robotics. B: talkativeness. C: scheme.

10. slough *n.*—A: soft breeze. B: heavy club. C: swamp.

11. spurious *adj.*—A: hasty. B: fake. C: livid.

12. nuptial *adj.*—A: just starting. B: relating to marriage. C: present during all seasons.

13. coxswain *n.*—A: innkeeper. B: secret lover. C: sailor in charge.

14. geoduck *n.*—A: earth tremor. B: wooden footstool. C: large Pacific clam.

15. plethora *n.*—A: person not of noble rank. B: abundance. C: spiritual journey.

Draw the Line

Try to draw this shape with one continuous line without lifting your pencil off the page and without any overlapping.

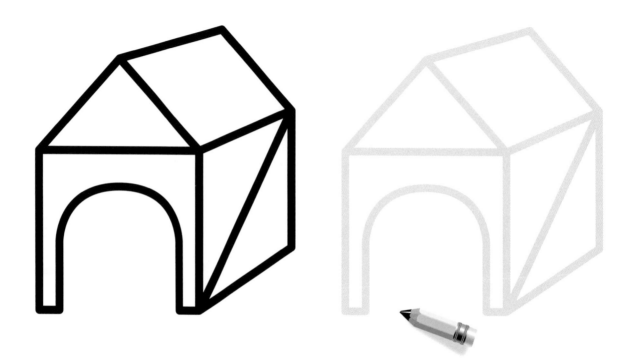

END GAME

The words you are seeking all have the letters END in them in the position indicated. When you have found all of the answers with help from the clues on the right, one column will reveal the END GAME word and give you a number.

—	—	—	—	—	**E**	**N**	**D**	To lengthen equally
—	—	—	**E**	**N**	**D**	—	—	Super
E	**N**	**D**	—	—	—	—	—	Lasting
—	—	—	**E**	**N**	**D**	—	—	Flowering plant

CROSSWORD St. Patrick's Day

ACROSS

1 Part of a door
5 Go on a tirade
9 Actress Gardner
12 October birthstone
13 Beige
14 Tub or container
15 Stretching exercises
16 St. Patrick's three-leaf symbol
18 Assign a rank to
20 Decorative edge
21 Ghouls
24 Actor John of Monty Python
25 Insert deeply
26 Name after Fannie or Sallie
27 Infant
28 A leprechaun's ___ of gold at the end of the rainbow
29 Actor Idris from *Pacific Rim*
33 Center
34 Slander
35 Like Wordsworth
39 To grow chompers
40 Military protection
41 Fly like an eagle
42 Irish poem
44 It equals width times height
48 Minnesota's most visited attraction (abbrev.)
49 All right
50 Not short
51 The A in Q&A (abbrev.)
52 Nevada city
53 Extinct bird

DOWN

1 Happiness
2 Military mailing address (abbrev.)
3 Periodical, for short
4 Stone kissed by the Irish
5 Takes a break
6 Tooth pain
7 Gun lobby group (abbrev.)
8 Rough and ___
9 On top of
10 Sins
11 It connects the leg bone to the foot bone
17 Pioneer Woman Drummond
19 Do the math
21 Month after Jan.
22 "___ Believer" by the Monkees (2 words)
23 ___ and flow
24 *The ___ in the Hat*
26 '60s style
28 Photo, for short
29 Ireland is the ___ Isle
30 "___ It Be" by the Beatles
31 "___, humbug!"
32 "My lips ___ sealed"
33 What the evil queen talked to
34 Caspian or Red
35 *Scarface* director Brian De ___
36 Large winter constellation
37 Actresses Stone and Watson
38 It is often stubbed
39 Japan's capital
41 Skim
43 Eisenhower nickname
45 Kanga's son
46 Finish
47 Gone by

Sunny

Where will the sun shine, if each arrow points in the direction of a spot where the symbol is located? The symbols cannot be next to each other vertically, horizontally or diagonally. A symbol cannot be placed on top of an arrow. We show one symbol.

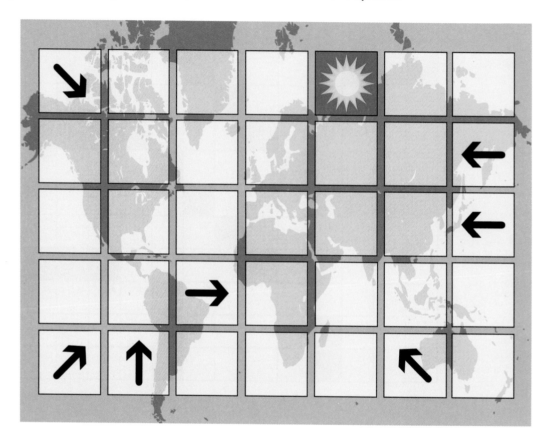

BLOCK ANAGRAM

Form the word that is described in the brackets with the letters above the grid. Extra letters are already in the right place.

TEA DRESS (hostess)

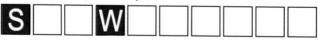

S _ _ W _ _ _ _ _

Word Sudoku

Complete the grid so that each row, each column and each 3 x 3 frame contains the nine letters from the black box below. The hidden nine-letter word is in the diagonal from top left to bottom right.

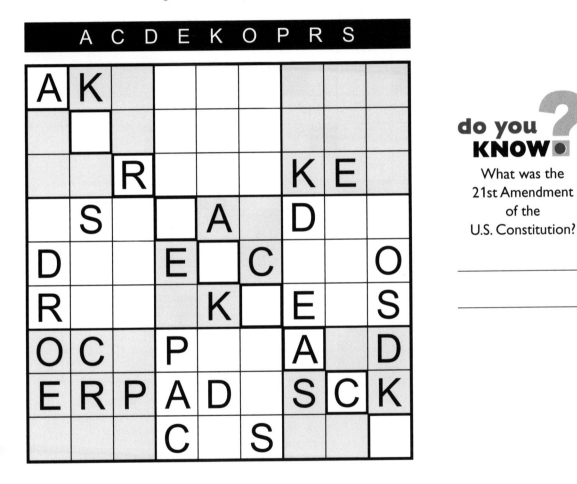

A C D E K O P R S

do you **KNOW?**

What was the
21st Amendment
of the
U.S. Constitution?

TRANSADDITION

Add two letters to **NOT IN ACCORD** and rearrange the rest to find a word with a connection to the original phrase.

ACROSS

1 Gangster gal
5 "He loves me" piece
10 Golfer Scott
14 Exchange premium
15 "I'm Looking ___ Four-Leaf Clover"
16 *She's Gotta Have It* girl
17 "*Aurora*" artist
18 *Life: A User's Manual* author Georges
19 Hexagram
20 Manhattan locale of the Dakota
23 Musical talent
24 French goose
25 Berlin's "Puttin' on ___"
29 Women's shoe styles
33 Golf legend Walter
34 "Amo, ___, I Love a Lass"
36 *The Guns of Navarone* actress Scala
37 New York Philharmonic home
41 "Bubble Bobble" console
42 50-oared ship of myth
43 Chair designer
44 Winwood in *The Misfits*
47 *CHiPS* star
49 Call for help
50 "If I ___": Eminem
51 Ellis Island attraction
60 Earring spot
61 Osprey claw
62 Greenwich Village neighbor
63 "The potted physician"
64 It belongs to thee
65 "Buy It Now" site
66 Purple fruit
67 *It Came From ___ Space* (1953)
68 *Alice in Wonderland* bird

DOWN

1 Alaimo of *Star Trek: DS9*
2 S-shaped molding
3 *Before You Sleep* novelist Ullmann
4 Vagrant
5 Andy Warhol's genre
6 Stunt-cyclist Knievel
7 U. of Maryland athlete
8 Territory
9 College stick sport
10 Respond to a knock
11 Be enamored
12 "'Tis a pity!"
13 Apu's Kwik-E-___
21 "Here's That ___ Day"
22 Young fox
25 Scottish clan chief
26 The privileged
27 Antonym for absorb
28 "Rumble in the Jungle" locale
29 Porsche SUV
30 Blue-headed lizard
31 In a heap
32 *Dancing With the Stars* dance
35 Lo mein additive
38 How Tiny Tim sang
39 Adjust a document setting
40 Made tougher
45 Think highly of
46 Gossett or Holtz
48 Black eye
51 "Fresh!" follow-up
52 Bridge fee
53 Hunt's "___ Ben Adhem"
54 Pearl City locale
55 *Pocahontas* hummingbird
56 Sole
57 Automated prefix
58 Jazz trumpeter Jones
59 Walk-the-dog toy

Cage the Animals

Draw lines to completely divide up the grid into small squares with exactly one animal per square. The squares should not overlap.

do you KNOW

Who created
Dr. Jekyll and
Mr. Hyde?

_____

_____

LETTERBLOCKS

Move the letterblocks around so that words are formed on top and below that you would associate with emotions. One block from the top row has been switched with a block from the bottom row.

Keep Going

Start on a blank square of your choice and connect as many blank squares as possible with one single continuous line. You can only connect squares along vertical and horizontal lines, not along diagonal lines. You must continue the connecting line up until the next obstacle, i.e., the rim of the box, a black square or a square that has already been used. You can change direction at any obstacle you meet. Each square can only be used once. The number of blank squares that will be left unused is marked in the upper square. There is more than one solution. We only show one solution.

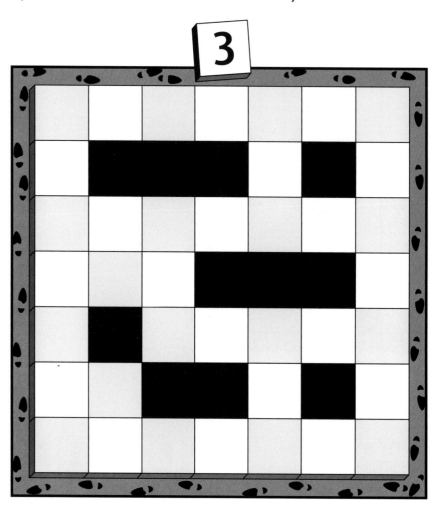

delete ONE

Delete one letter from
ON SCALE OF SINS
and rearrange the rest to find an enclosed booth.

CROSSWORD Sleuths

ACROSS

1 Anglo-Saxon bard
5 #
10 Cabbage salad
14 *Deus* ___ (1976 sci-fi novel)
15 Exactly opposite
16 Mother of Pollux
17 Agatha Christie sleuth
19 Kline in *The Squid and the Whale*
20 Defeats
21 Like five-star hotels
23 Net-worth factor
24 Jewish month
25 Smell awful
27 Lettering aid
30 Printer cartridge
33 Age
35 Tiller's tool
36 Parodied
37 "___ Johnny!"
38 FedExed
39 Southern Iran city
40 Hawkeye Stater
41 U.S. Open winner Safin
42 "Heh-heh," for one
44 Use a rotary phone
46 "Able ___ ere ..."
47 Assistant for Hillary
51 Alligator pear
54 Scintillates
55 "The Persistence of Memory" painter
56 Fictional TV sleuth
58 "A" in code
59 Ache
60 *Breathing Lessons* author Tyler
61 Command to Rover
62 All filled up
63 Knead homophone

DOWN

1 Disney lion
2 Has a bawl
3 Brewery kilns
4 Annoyed
5 Exiguous
6 ___ d'oeuvres
7 Grossglockner, e.g.
8 Chest rattle
9 Bishops and monsignors
10 Catchphrase
11 Ross Macdonald sleuth
12 Yemen capital
13 Kind of ad
18 Length unit
22 First place
26 Mardi Gras group
27 Shell out
28 Macbeth's burial isle
29 Riga resident
30 Barbershop powder
31 Aquarium beauty
32 Rex Stout sleuth
34 *Star Trek* producer Behr
37 Special times
38 Willy Loman, for one
40 "___ most unusual day..."
41 Hunter of the PGA
43 Kind of profiling
45 *Cast Away* setting
48 Geneva river
49 Al dente order
50 Questioned
51 Esau's wife
52 Batman's friend Vicki
53 Ancient Greek concert halls
54 Prometheus stole it
57 Informant

Still a novelty for most Americans, television was hitting its stride by 1952. With shows like *Dragnet* and *I Love Lucy* reaching millions, networks pushed for fast hits. Some, like *Gang Busters*, an early true-crime show, didn't last. But a handful of programs from the '52-'53 season would prove to have incredible staying power.

CAN YOU NAME THESE FAMOUS SHOWS, WHICH ALL STARTED THAT YEAR?

1 The first show to feature that crazy new sound—rock 'n' roll—is broadcast (under a slightly different name at the time) from Philadelphia. In a few short years, Dick Clark would take over as host.

_____

2 This comedy starred a real husband and wife and, later, their two sons. The set was an exact replica of the family's actual Hollywood house.

_____

3 This was a panel game show similar to *What's My Line?*

_____

4 It featured a grown man in tights whose alter ego was a hunky newspaper reporter.

_____

5 The chubby star's signature phrases were "And awa-a-a-y we go" and "How sweet it is!"

_____

6 This one starred Eve Arden as a wise-cracking high school English teacher.

_____

TEST YOUR RECALL

What cereal was first introduced in 1952 that featured a tiger?

_____

Sudoku

Fill in the grid so that each row, each column and each 3 x 3 frame contains every number from 1 to 9.

				2			6	
2		6		8		1		9
5			1		7			
6					1	7		
	5	7				2	4	
		8	4					6
			8		6			5
1		4		9		3		2
	9			1				

do you KNOW?

Whose story is Hitchcock's *The Birds* based on?

_____

_____

triVia • At the 1936 Berlin Olympics, German leader Adolf Hitler walked out of the games when a black American athlete won his fourth gold medal.

What was the athlete's name?

_____

CROSSWORD City Nicknames

ACROSS

1 Chrysler engine
5 *Thaïs* is one
10 Revival cry
14 Esfahan locale
15 Carpenters drummer
16 *Reader's Digest* cofounder Wallace
17 "Paris of the Plains"
19 Roman 1052
20 Eyeball
21 Masonry tool
23 *A Man for All* ___ (1966)
24 Capital of 29 Across
25 Airport security org.
26 Humidifier mist
29 *Lost Horizon* land
32 "Ain't That a Shame" singer Pat
33 Big Island's Mauna ___
34 Thoroughfare
35 Antler feature
36 Book-lined rooms
37 Saddlery tool
38 Eye drops
39 Sleazy
40 Job's virtue
42 *Once Upon a Mattress* legume
43 "Goodnight" girl
44 "Adieu"
48 Goddess of fruitful abundance
50 Woebegone
51 Warwickshire river
52 "The Big Easy"
54 Naples neighbor
55 Nonsense
56 Commedia dell'___
57 Baldwin in *The Departed*
58 More balanced
59 A shade of blue

DOWN

1 Nature walks
2 Answering machine button
3 Big ray
4 Took a firm stand
5 Baiul on ice
6 Accords
7 "... 15 miles on the ___ Canal"
8 Dampen flax
9 Cole Porter's "___ Goes"
10 "Close but no cigar"
11 "Brew City"
12 *Dawn* author Wiesel
13 Spike
18 "It's ___ Unusual Day"
22 Level, in London
24 Birds on Canadian coins
26 Dudley in *Santa Claus*
27 Cleave
28 Simple
29 Saint Andrews hazard
30 Davenport site
31 "Charm City"
32 "___ yourself!"
35 Baseball flags
36 Collection agency's target
38 *Not Another* ___ *Movie* (2001)
39 1988 Olympics host city
41 Paradoxical
42 "For richer, for ___ ..."
44 Fumble around
45 Bugle sound
46 Yiddish busybody
47 Ford of the 1950s
48 Sunblock ingredient
49 Squashed circle
50 Jenna Bush Hager, to sister Barbara
53 Mariano Rivera stat

BRAINSNACK® All Square

Move three matches to make two squares.

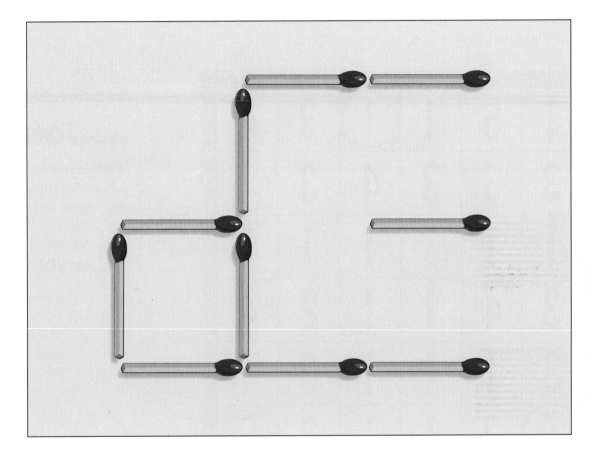

DOODLE PUZZLE

A doodle puzzle is a combination of images, letters and/or numbers that represent a word or a concept. If you cannot solve a doodle puzzle, do not look at the answer right away. Think hard—and outside the box.

Sport Maze

Draw the shortest way from the ball to the goal. You can only move along vertical and horizontal lines, not along diagonal lines. The figure on each square indicates the number of squares the ball must be moved in the same direction. You can change direction at each stop.

1	5	1	1	3	4
3	3	3	4	3	1
1	1	3	1	1	4
3	4	1	1	2	4
3	1	1	1	3	1
	2	1	1	3	5

change ONE

Change one letter in each of these two words to form a common two-word phrase.

BUSH SOUR

ONE LETTER LESS OR MORE

The word on the right side contains the letters of the word on the left side plus or minus the letter in the middle. One letter is already in the right place.

F A C E L I F T -E ☐ ☐ ☐ ☐ C ☐

CROSSWORD Pet Cats

ACROSS

1 *Lemony Snicket* evil count
5 ___ zirconia
10 Nullify a correction
14 TriBeCa neighbor
15 *Androcles and the Lion* locale
16 Not that
17 John in *Tarantula*
18 "___ Constant Sorrow"
19 Chaplin in *Quantum of Solace*
20 Jim Davis cat
22 One close to the soil
24 Arouses admiration in
25 1965 march site
26 "... ___ yellow submarine"
27 Tiffani of *White Collar*
30 Aerosol sprays
33 Le Pont-Neuf spans it
34 Dockworker's org.
35 Acuff and Clark
36 Bugle sound
37 Piece of cake
38 Cockney inferno
39 At the ready
40 "1 inch = 10 miles," e.g.
41 Grows steadily
43 Pie ___ mode
44 Live and breathe
45 Churchill Downs sights
49 Samples
51 The Simpsons' first cat
52 Dortmund duck
53 Time after time
55 "Fits you to ___!"
56 Egyptian sun god
57 Bench-clearer
58 Auberjonois of *Deep Space Nine*
59 Shopping place
60 Samurai weapon
61 "Darn!"

DOWN

1 Missouri tributary
2 *South Pacific* director
3 ___ *Day's Night* (1964)
4 Gives up
5 "Action!" preceder
6 Russian peaks
7 Give a little
8 Sea goddess who saved Odysseus
9 Jolt in Jolt
10 Weather radar red areas
11 Mary McDhui's pet cat
12 ___ *kleine Nachtmusik*
13 Imperialist of yore
21 McKellen and McEwan
23 Not aweather
25 Tank top
27 Eye drops
28 Mideast carrier
29 A barber may shave this
30 Talking horse
31 Captive of Hercules
32 Granny's pet cat
33 "George Washington ___ Here"
36 Flowers
37 Sword sheath
39 "You can't pray ___"
40 Shredded dish
42 Breadth
43 Answered (for)
45 "That'll teach you!" look
46 Subsequently
47 Kagan of the Supreme Court
48 Icy precip
49 Uniformed unit
50 Pilaster
51 Battle of Normandy site
54 A handful of

Match Maker

Move two matches to complete the formula.

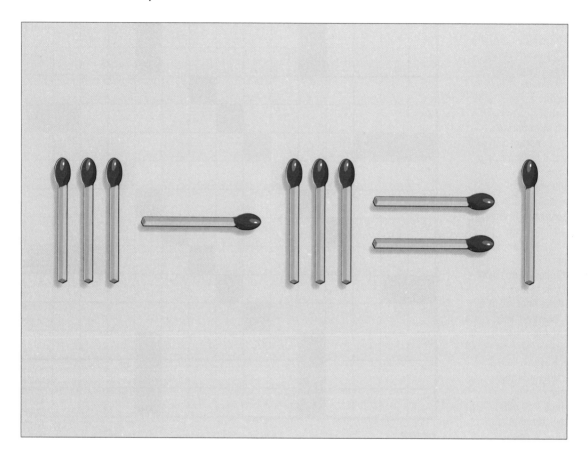

BLOCK ANAGRAM

Form the words that are described in the brackets with the letters above the grid. Extra letters are already in the right place.

MBA Cobra   (the 44th)

| | A | | | K | | | A | |

WORD SEARCH Wedding Bells

All the words are hidden vertically, horizontally or diagonally—
in both directions.

```
Q T J T R E T R A G H B B Z U N R J B
T O F K P O V B V P I L I C E N S E M
X E L X R L M O O R G O T F D J C E V
Z R A G O O D U L Y G K M L M Y Q K E
G R A A M X V Q P V V G T F I H Y P D
Y N J I I L R U A B B U L Q N D N F H
G G Y P S T E E F O G O Z V I N O K V
P Q N C E F V T Y O W O O E S O M N F
H D T T A T D P W E P W X O T M E O M
I J E T E L M N R Q S C O W E A R I W
W R K O I D W G Q A R W O Z R I E T K
E J S A H T I E K Y A L A W C D C P T
I N I S L R K R U E I O Z A I A W E L
I Y H T L I G C B P S F W O H F K C B
P B I Y K L E B R U L N N C I Y E E I
T B B O L K Z V Y Z E X R L Z N X R H
F N Q T I D C A V A Z U D N A B S U H
R T N P Q V V H S K H O N E Y M O O N
P U L U C P P F D C T O D E X U T S E
```

- AISLE
- DIAMOND
- HUSBAND
- RECEPTION
- BOUQUET
- FLOWER GIRL
- LICENSE
- TOAST
- BRIDE
- GARTER
- LOVE
- TUXEDO
- CAKE
- GOWN
- MINISTER
- VEIL
- CEREMONY
- GROOM
- ORGAN
- VOWS
- CHURCH
- HONEYMOON
- PROMISE
- WIFE

CROSSWORD # April Showers

ACROSS

1 ___ and butter pickles
6 Eureka!
9 Address for a gentleman
12 Early video game brand
13 Police officer
14 Cow's sound
15 ___ firma (Earth)
16 *Early ___ Rain* by Peter, Paul and Mary
18 1984 film *The Woman ___* (2 words)
20 "I cannot tell ___" (2 words)
21 ___ *Rainy Night* by Eddie Rabbitt (3 words)
24 ___ *America Singing* by Walt Whitman (2 words)
25 Slangy refusal
26 *Don't Let the Rain Come ___* by the Serendipity Singers
29 Slice
30 Fibbers
31 Facial bone
34 *It Ain't Gonna Rain No ___*, traditional song
35 A song for one
36 Log home
40 ___ *in the Rain* by Gene Kelly
42 Actor Alda
43 ___ Dame
45 *Somewhere Over the ___* by Judy Garland
47 Eagle's nest
51 Ambulance worker (abbrev.)
52 Employ
53 Place for the 50-meter dash
54 Emergency signal
55 Scarlet
56 ___ Lauder cosmetics

DOWN

1 Baseball ___
2 ___ 66 (abbrev.)
3 Spot for a piercing
4 Show up
5 Actress Lane
6 Wile E Coyote's preferred brand
7 Little Red Riding ___
8 Month before May (abbrev.)
9 Grin
10 Ancient area of Turkey
11 Movie critic Ebert
17 25 Across synonym
19 It has AM and FM settings
21 Business abbreviation
22 ___ Gehrig
23 Choose
24 ___ and outs
27 Paddle
28 Pull something from someone's grasp
30 Letters after IJK
31 Run
32 Boxer Muhammad
33 Succeeded
35 Laughs evilly
36 Has feelings
37 San Antonio attraction
38 Puts a worm on a hook
39 Holiday ___ Express
41 Furious
43 Win by a ___
44 Was in debt
46 Prickly seed
48 Long-tailed rodent
49 Freezer item
50 Squeeze out

BRAINSNACK® Believe Your Eyes

Which of the groups (1–6) of squares actually include parallelograms?

Form the words that are described in the brackets with the letters above the grid. Extra letters are already in the right place.

All melons   (causes food poisoning)

									A

Insulation

What is the order of the layers of insulation (1-5) that will replace the question marks?
Answer like this: 1255.

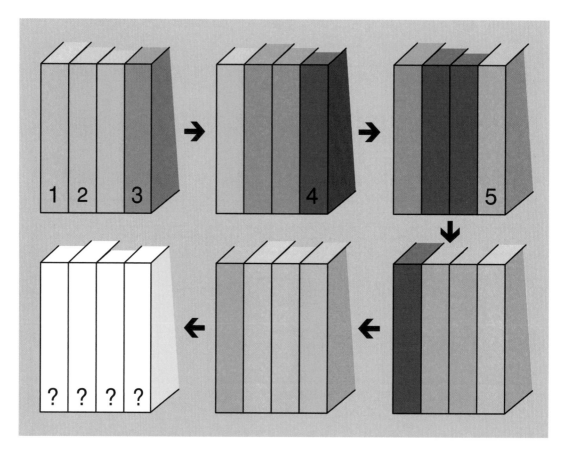

DOODLE PUZZLE

A doodle puzzle is a combination of images, letters and/or numbers that represent a word or a concept. If you cannot solve a doodle puzzle, do not look at the answer right away. Think hard—and outside the box.

Binairo

Complete the grid with zeros and ones until there are 6 zeros and 6 ones in every row and every column. No more than two of the same number can be next to or under each other. Rows or columns with exactly the same content are not allowed. There is only one valid solution.

					I		I				
						I		I			I
O	I		I		I						I
								O			
		O		O	O			O			
		O				I				I	
						O					
	O										
		O	O			I	I		I		
						I				O	
I				I			O			O	
	I		I		O	O			I		

do you KNOW?

What does the Latin phrase *caveat emptor* mean?

_____

_____

REPOSITION PREPOSITION

Unscramble **I DID NOTATION** and find a three-word preposition.

_____

A range of wars, a range of questions: How well will you do?

1. In which war was the image of Uncle Sam first used?

   a. War of 1812
   b. Civil War
   c. World War I
   d. World War II

2. What killed the most soldiers during the Civil War?

   a. Hunger
   b. Disease
   c. Bullets
   d. Exposure

3. Which state was not a Confederate state?

   a. Kansas
   b. Florida
   c. Texas
   d. Louisiana

4. The United States declared war against which country in 1812?

   a. France
   b. Germany
   c. Britain
   d. Mexico

5. Which war saw the introduction of the income tax?

   a. Revolutionary War
   b. Civil War
   c. World War I
   d. World War II

6. In which century was the Mexican War?

   a. 17th
   b. 18th
   c. 19th
   d. 20th

7. Under which U.S. president were the last American troops withdrawn from Vietnam?

   a. Lyndon Johnson
   b. Richard Nixon
   c. Gerald Ford
   d. Ronald Reagan

8. What country did Iraq invade that led to the Persian Gulf War?

   a. Iran
   b. Afghanistan
   c. Israel
   d. Kuwait

9. During the Civil War, which side drafted soldiers?

   a. The Union
   b. The Confederacy
   c. Both
   d. Neither

10. About 50,000 soldiers were killed in which Civil War battle?

   a. Battle of Gettysburg
   b. Battle of Bull Run
   c. Battle of Fredericksburg
   d. Battle of Burgess' Mill

CROSSWORD Best-Sellers #1

ACROSS

1 "Please respond"
5 Florida citrus center
10 Bushy hairstyle
14 Buckeye State
15 Name on a check
16 Office wear
17 Tina Fey best-seller
19 Shutter strip
20 Beach shrinkage
21 Board game with discs
23 Round robin
24 Sage, e.g.
25 Shaped glass
27 "Day Tripper" group
30 Kiddie
33 Butler of fiction
35 "Hail, Caesar!"
36 Like a blue moon
37 Round bread loaf
38 A tug may tow it
39 1969 Nobel Peace Prize group
40 Areca nut
41 "Monopoly" ship, e.g.
42 Pep-rally blaze
44 Big-budget film
46 Cod cousin
47 *Super 8* director
51 Cataclysmic
54 Balkan state
55 12th Hebrew month
56 Jim Butcher best-seller
58 Stand up
59 Scary
60 *Lord of the Rings* creatures
61 "___ there, done that!"
62 O'Reilly of *M*A*S*H*
63 Area below Greenwich Village

DOWN

1 Graduation wear
2 Seaboard
3 Baseball cap part
4 Workable
5 Act against
6 *Brian's Song* Emmy nominee
7 *Anthem* author Rand
8 *American Psycho* actor Jared
9 Affected lover of beauty
10 Affirm
11 Brad Thor best-seller
12 100 Iranian dinars
13 *A Fish Called Wanda* character
18 Road sign
22 Qualifying race
26 Penned
27 *Beauty and the Beast* beauty
28 Ancient cry of revelry
29 Stitched
30 Nursery bed
31 Sundog
32 John Hart best-seller
34 Color
37 Tom in *Major League*
38 "Know thyself" philosopher
40 Schwinn product
41 *They Call Me MISTER ___* (1970)
43 Conquered
45 Be deceitful
48 "That's ___!" ("Don't do that!")
49 Amusement
50 Final authority
51 Action word
52 Nastase of tennis
53 "Take ___ Train"
54 Large land mass
57 O'Hare airport code

Meet the Parents

ACROSS

1 In the matter of
5 In the company of
10 Starchy veggie
14 *Return of the Jedi* princess
15 Melancholy
16 Jackrabbit
17 Bearded scythe-carrier
19 October gem
20 Smoke-and-mirrors act
21 Esprit de corps
23 Storm center
24 Spanish 101 verb
25 Fabric
26 Female swan
27 Contradicted
30 Eternal City resident
33 Bloom in *High Plains Drifter*
34 "It Had to Be ___"
35 ___ the crack of dawn
36 Spills the beans
37 Run in neutral
38 Breach
39 Fragrant rootstock
40 Comic-strip segment
41 Small pony
43 *American Beauty* director Mendes
44 Alpine river
45 Barnyard enclosure
46 Cleveland–Akron dir.
49 *Jeopardy!* contestants
51 Points of view
53 Tamiroff in *Lord Jim*
54 NYC Italian restaurant of yore
56 Cryptic character
57 Like helium
58 Figure skater Lipinski
59 Annie Oakley
60 Pitchfork features
61 Pretentious

DOWN

1 2004 Jude Law role
2 Big name in mattresses
3 Heading
4 Pearl Harbor locale
5 Brody in *The Pianist*
6 Outboard
7 Lena of *Alias*
8 ___ de plume
9 Mischiefmakers
10 Bermuda ___
11 *Surprise* symphony composer
12 Kazakhstan river
13 Take-out order
18 Steel city in the Ruhr
22 Charlie Chaplin's wife
25 Bernstein and Lewis
26 Sajak or Riley
27 Arctic
28 A daughter of Eurytus
29 *Hamlet* climax
30 They're taken out and beaten
31 Aquarium beauty
32 Radio soap opera (1933–49)
33 *20,000 Leagues Under the Sea* author
36 Convey
37 ___ *Legend* (2007)
39 Genus of swans
40 Virginia heard in 32 Down
42 Movie melodies
43 Wading birds
45 Fifth tire
46 Marine school finder
47 *Hägar the Horrible* dog
48 *A Modest Proposal* is one
49 Senior lobby
50 Antarctic bird
51 Telltale sign
52 9th Greek letter
55 Singer DiFranco

Cage the Animals

Draw lines to completely divide up the grid into small squares with exactly one animal per square. The squares should not overlap.

do you KNOW?

Name the pig leader in Orwell's *Animal Farm*.

_____

_____

LETTERBLOCKS

Move the letterblocks around so that words are formed on top and below that you would associate with school. Two blocks from the top row have been switched with blocks from the bottom row.

Circle Grams

Try to find the word formed by the letters. Hint: The trick is figuring out where to start.

1.

A U Q
L
I Y
T

2.

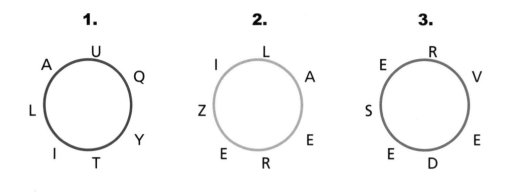

3.

E R V
S E
E D

4.

P T S
I
A I
N

5.

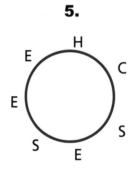

E H C
E
S S
E

6.

E A T
H E
T R

7.

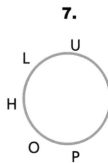

L U F
H
O E
P

8.

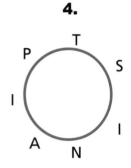

I M O
N S
O U

9.

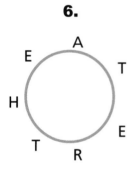

M O D
E B
N A

CROSSWORD # Wall Street Symbolism

ACROSS

1 Big Board "adjustment"
5 Badlands rise
9 Mature efts
14 Aussie leaper
15 "Want ___ a secret?"
16 Yahoo! letter
17 MSFT is its symbol
19 Christopher Robin's creator
20 Coach
21 Turned to slush
22 Acting too hastily
23 Acted (as)
24 Dream up
27 Kirghiz range
28 Gerund suffix
31 Dead letter, in post office talk
32 *Wheel of Fortune* turns
33 Mrs. bear
34 Word to the queue
35 Ins and outs
36 Pay to play
37 "Hang On to Your ___": Beach Boys
38 "Get ___ of yourself!"
39 *Primary Colors* author
40 *A Beautiful Mind* director Howard
41 Be enamored
42 Coral creatures
43 Lost in reverie
45 Air: Comb. form
46 Aussie swimmer Ian
48 Cotton Belt state
52 Capital of Morocco
53 MCD is its symbol
54 Cronelike
55 Indonesia's ___ Islands
56 Lean meat cut
57 Became colorless
58 That girl's
59 Pentax attachment

DOWN

1 Moore in *G.I. Jane*
2 Decimation
3 Dungeons & Dragons creatures
4 *Mona Lisa,* for one
5 Apply improperly
6 Methuselah's father
7 Ice-cream type
8 *A Bug's Life* bug
9 Archenemy
10 *Dirty Dancing* director Ardolino
11 DIS is its symbol
12 Small part of a spork
13 *Call of the Wild* vehicle
18 Deliver a keynote
21 Bewails
23 Applied (oneself)
24 More intimate
25 Dora the Explorer's cousin
26 XOM is its symbol
27 Singer Fiona
29 "Reward" for poor service
30 Actress Verdon and others
32 Smutty
35 Lake Geneva feeder
36 Completely
38 Accepted by vote
39 114-chapter book
42 Souchong alternatives
44 Benedict XVI's cape
45 Deep passion
46 "Shut your ___!"
47 Mandlikova of tennis
48 Lot measure
49 Gin fruit
50 Tennis score
51 1040 IDs
53 ___-jongg

Keep Going

Start on a blank square of your choice and connect as many blank squares as possible with one single continuous line. You can only connect squares along vertical and horizontal lines, not along diagonal lines. You must continue the connecting line up until the next obstacle, i.e., the rim of the box, a black square or a square that has already been used. You can change direction at any obstacle you meet. Each square can only be used once. The number of blank squares that will be left unused is marked in the upper square. There is more than one solution. We only show one solution.

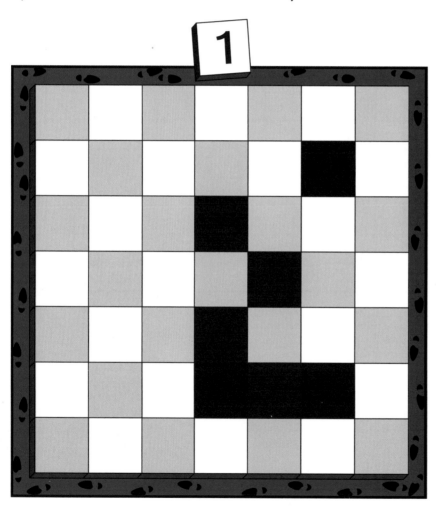

BRAINSNACK® Rocket

Use the five puzzle pieces in the rectangle to build the rocket next to it.
The puzzle pieces must not overlap.

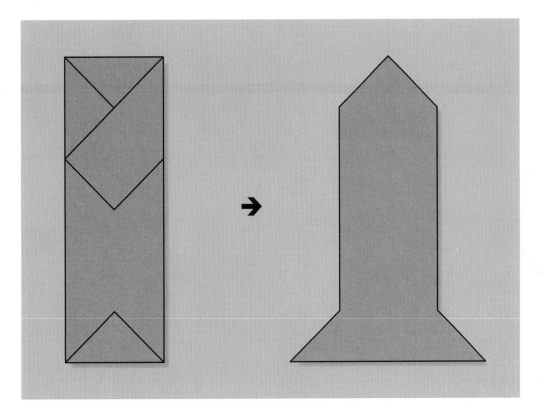

LETTER LINE

Put a letter in each of the squares below to make a word which will "bring help from above."

These numbered clues refer to other words which can be made from the whole:

9 2 10 5 2 ITALIAN STAPLE; 9 2 3 3 7 5 FEATHERED FRIEND;
3 7 5 7 3 MECHANICAL DEVICE; 10 7 2 9 SITCOM; 10 9 7 7 3 TRAIL

1	2	3	4	5	6	7	8	9	10

CROSSWORD — Olympic Host Cities

ACROSS

1 Barked comments
5 2 x 4, e.g.
10 "Take a Chance on Me" group
14 Vault
15 *The Sandbox* playwright
16 Round bread of India
17 1980 Olympics host city
19 *True* ___ (2010)
20 Winter stalactites
21 Calls the shots
23 Narrow grooves
24 "Anything Goes" composer Porter
25 Top condition
27 *Kojak* star
30 "When Joanna ___ Me"
33 Elliptical
35 *Ghost* psychic ___ Mae Brown
36 "___ Old Cowhand"
37 Fall off
38 Presently
39 Velvet add-on
40 Printing daggers
41 Facsimile
42 Amazing
44 Tasso's patron
46 Blue Bonnet, for one
47 Dr. Welby
51 Altercation at Citi Field
54 Prince of the comics
55 Gutter locale
56 1968 Olympics host city
58 Justify
59 Smart-___
60 Bittersweet coating
61 Saucy
62 Stows cargo
63 *Mikado* blade

DOWN

1 "___ forgiven!"
2 Jerk the knee
3 Hindu beggar
4 Sample for the lab
5 Whalebone
6 Spanish waves
7 *Desperate Housewives* network
8 "Green Hornet" Britt
9 Inscribe personally
10 Lansbury in *Death on the Nile*
11 1992 Olympics host city
12 Worms
13 Myrmecology study
18 Kilt pattern
22 Act the nomad
26 Maguire in *Spider-Man*
27 *Danses gothiques* composer
28 Sick as ___
29 Mentally healthy
30 Stead
31 Prophetic sign
32 2010 Olympics host city
34 *At First Sight* star Kilmer
37 Untypical
38 Yachting cup
40 "___ penny, two ..."
41 *Cosmicomics* author Calvino
43 "Fat" Cosby character
45 Loud kisses
48 Terrier breed
49 Loosen laces
50 Vogue
51 Cradle grain
52 "Where ___ All the Flowers Gone?"
53 Gymnastics coach Karolyi
54 Bad habit
57 Marked a box

Word Sudoku

Complete the grid so that each row, each column and each 3 x 3 frame contains the nine letters from the black box below. The hidden nine-letter word is in the diagonal from top left to bottom right.

A C E H M N O R Z

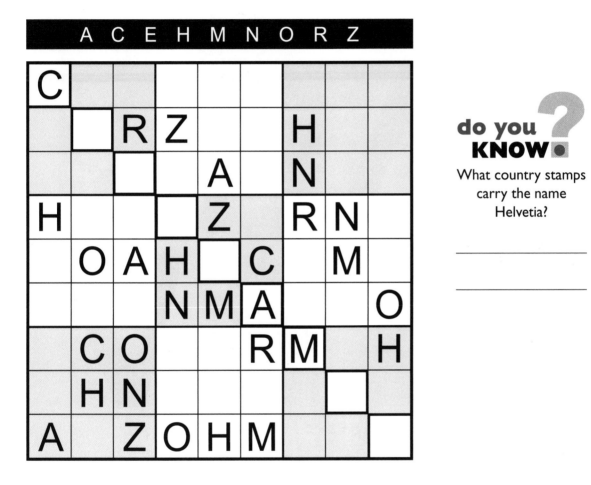

do you KNOW?

What country stamps carry the name Helvetia?

_____

_____

Spot the Differences

Find the nine differences between the images.

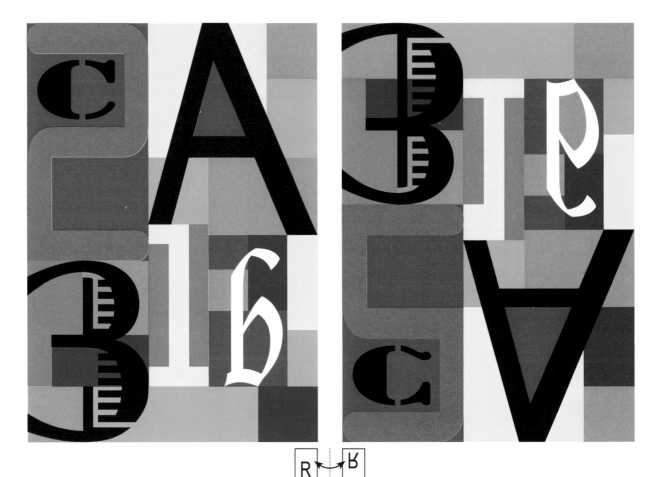

BLOCK ANAGRAM

Form the words that are described in the brackets with the letters above the grid. Extra letters are already in the right place.

Rituals (country and continent)

					A		A

CROSSWORD Arbor Day

ACROSS

1 State tree of TX
6 Auto
9 Orlando's state (abbrev.)
12 Run away and marry
13 Poetic tribute
14 ___ and reel
15 English beauty ___ Middleton
16 State tree of MO and VA, the flowering ___
18 Had a meal
20 Dishwasher setting
21 State tree of WA, the western ___
25 Sign on the "In" door
26 Track shape
27 *Every Thing* ___ by Shel Silverstein (2 words)
29 Attains
30 Chicken part
31 Again
35 Part of a ship
36 Turkish money
37 44th president
41 State tree of OR, the ___ fir
43 Form of renewable energy
44 Loneliest number
45 State tree of LA, the bald ___
48 Rocky ridge
52 Ginger ___
53 Electric swimmer
54 Goes higher
55 Cartoon characters ___ and Stimpy
56 Mother's Day month
57 State tree of NY, VT, WI and WV, the sugar ___

DOWN

1 Type of rally
2 Inventor Whitney
3 Police officer
4 Disgusts
5 Groovy
6 A white fish
7 *Much* ___ *About Nothing*
8 Lament
9 Where cold air meets warm air
10 Not secured tightly
11 Small viper
17 Succeed
19 School, in French
21 Domestic swine
22 The night before a big event
23 Floor cloth
24 Struck a blow with part of the leg
28 Structure made of snow and ice
31 Country in NW Africa
32 Nothing
33 Time period
34 Used to be
35 Basketball player Abdul-Jabbar
37 Academy Award
38 Scottish singer Susan
39 Word describing mountainous central Europe
40 Spoil
42 Take away weapons
46 Body of salt water
47 Tricky
49 Sixth sense
50 ___ Aviv, Israel
51 Compass direction opposite WNW

Sudoku Twin

Fill in the grid so that each row, each column and each 3 x 3 frame contains every number from 1 to 9. A sudoku twin is two connected 9 x 9 sudokus.

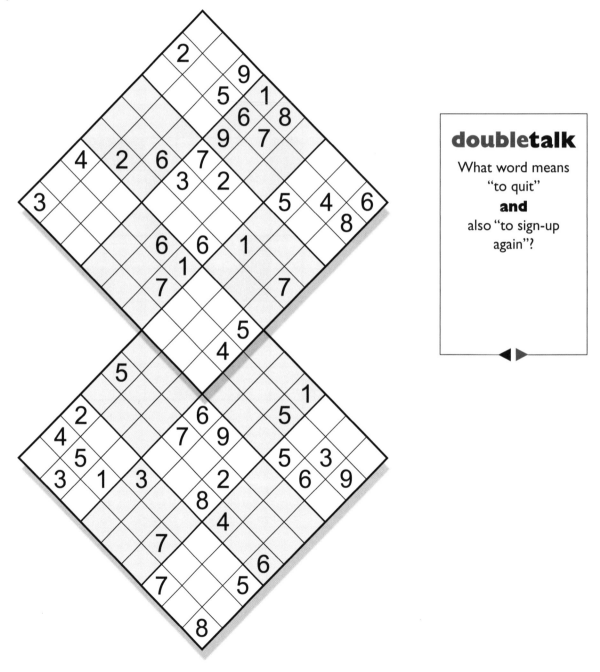

Sport Maze

Draw the shortest way from the ball to the goal. You can only move along vertical and horizontal lines, not along diagonal lines. The figure on each square indicates the number of squares the ball must be moved in the same direction. You can change direction at each stop.

2	1	2	2	3	2
3	1	2	2	3	5
2	2	2	3	2	3
5	1	3	1	4	5
4	2	4	1	4	5
	3	1	4	4	3

change ONE

Change one letter in each of these two words to form a common two-word phrase.

SAD FLOOD

ONE LETTER LESS OR MORE

The word on the right side contains the letters of the word on the left side plus or minus the letter in the middle. One letter is already in the right place.

H A I R L I N E -I □ N □ □ □ □ □

CROSSWORD # Catching Some Zs

ACROSS

1 Chase flies
5 Conical dwelling
10 Somewhat
14 Eugene O'Neill's daughter
15 *My Fair Lady* heroine
16 Hindu sacred books
17 Certain radar detector
19 Garlic quality
20 Adriatic port
21 Rapscallions
23 *The Life of Christ* frescoist
24 At the home of
25 Blue Nile source lake
27 Audacity
30 Postpone
33 Oliver's porridge
35 Lesser of *Seinfeld*
36 Wood stork
37 Adds color
38 Hit on the head
39 *Frasier* character
40 Jacob Marley, for one
41 Chaplain
42 Agents of biochemical change
44 Mayonnaise ingredient
46 Lewd look
47 Muslim ruler
51 Rigby of song
54 Dolphins' order
55 "Love ___ leave me ..." (ABBA lyric)
56 They're hot at Domino's
58 Badly claw
59 Bottled Alpine water
60 Uncle's wife
61 A bit pretentious
62 Mall anchor, frequently
63 German admiral of WWI

DOWN

1 Head of Germany?
2 Muslim maid of paradise
3 Nero's birthplace
4 Newspaper names
5 Ancient German
6 Otherwise
7 Speedway area
8 Israeli statesman Weizman
9 Otitis symptoms
10 Long-legged bird
11 Flabbergasted
12 Pop hero
13 Seamen, slangily
18 Rigel, for one
22 Synagogue
26 Currency allowances
27 ___ Sark
28 Alligator ___ (avocado)
29 Last Stuart queen
30 Like some straits
31 Black, to bards
32 End weakly
34 Nursing home workers
37 Basic procedures
38 Turkish desserts
40 DEA agents
41 Athenian philosopher
43 Annual
45 Oodles
48 Acquire a wintry covering
49 Slant-cut pasta
50 "Marry in ___ ..."
51 Thompson in *Junior*
52 Sitcom producer Norman
53 Tear apart
54 Absolute ruler
57 Pakistan president (1978–88)

Sudoku

Fill in the grid so that each row, each column and each 3 x 3 frame contains every number from 1 to 9.

			9		1			5
		5		6			9	
	6	2	4					8
		9		2		3		
	7						6	
		8		5		9		
5					3	4	7	
	2			4		8		
7			6		8			

do you KNOW?

Who directed the film *Titanic?*

_____

_____

triVia • Marion Michael Morrison was the real name of one of Hollywood's greatest stars, an all-American hero who personified the frontier spirit.

What was his screen name?

_____

Be Mine

All the words are hidden vertically, horizontally or diagonally—
in both directions.

```
V M E O P T C W C D G L R D Y U N S C
S S G O D N E I K M F H A I G R X N O
F P A S S I O N N I A T U S T R A E H
X S B L Z G H S P P E T S G Z O D Z H
S A O S W Y W Z R G V J E U S H Y U Q
W V Q U C Q N C K A A P S A S J O A C
E F B Z H Z V W L Z A D O R L M E E R
E P U V E M S E Q V R D R O A O A B J
T I Y R G S N E C E J P N J C H D J I
H Y O H I T C V A N V F Q B E Z I M D
E D L K I E G O R U U D L Q O K P I G
A F T N H T G A D S Y E Q O T I U N T
R O E F Y A L R D G H A J E W T C D I
T E E R X L Q L S T M A F R I E N D E
X D R F R O T H C A N D Y I O N R D I
A R Z X P C P S A X M S B X A L L S E
W N U Z D O C T K D R E N N I D B R S
R T A P E H V M N Z P G Y B P P R J T
L N E K R C X B E D A N E R E S P P U
```

- ADORE
- DATE
- KISS
- RED
- BEAU
- DINNER
- LACE
- ROSES
- CANDY
- FLOWERS
- LOVE
- SERENADE
- CARD
- FRIEND
- MATE
- SWEETHEART
- CHOCOLATE
- HEARTS
- PASSION
- VALENTINE
- CUPID
- HUGS
- POEM
- VENUS

TRIVIA QUIZ I'll Have a Cold One!

Beer is the most popular drink in the world. What's your brew?

1. The German beer glass known as a mass krug holds how much beer?

_____

2. Kriek is brewed with what type of fruit?

_____

3. Stout or porter such as Guinness gets its dark, thick characteristics because what is done to the barley malt?

_____

4. The ale style known as IPA came about because British brewers realized that the strongly hopped ale would better survive the long transit to where?

_____

5. What's the name of the Belgian style of beer that is naturally fermented using wild yeasts?

_____

6. What country drinks the most beer per capita?

_____

7. Why is some beer preferably drunk at room temperature rather than chilled?

_____

8. In general, ales tend to have fruity, more complex aromas while lagers taste smoother and crisper. What makes the difference between them?

_____

TEST YOUR RECALL

How many slogans can you pair with the frothy brand each describes?

1. Budweiser	A	The Champagne of Beers
2. Coors	B	Good Things Come to Those Who Wait
3. Corona	C	Brewed with Pure Rocky Mountain Spring Water
4. Foster's	D	Reassuringly Expensive
5. Guinness	E	Miles Away from Ordinary
6. Miller High Life	F	The Beer That Made Milwaukee Famous
7. Old Milwaukee	G	The King of Beers
8. Schlitz	H	Tastes As Great As Its Name
9. Stella Artois	I	Australian for Beer

Body Language

When the ancient Greeks inscribed the phrase "Know thyself" at the temple of Apollo, we're pretty sure they meant it in the philosophical sense.

. . . .

But how well do you know thyself in a physical sense?

1. mental *adj.*—of or relating to … A: the navel. B: the chin. C: the hands or feet.

2. visage *n.*—A: face. B: lens of the eye. C: type of birthmark.

3. hirsute adj.—A: bent over with hands on knees. B: barrel-chested. C: hairy.

4. pectoral *adj.*—A: of the side. B: of the back. C: of the chest.

5. corpulent adj.—A: of or relating to the skull. B: bulky or stout. C: frail, as a bone.

6. alopecia *n.*—A: skin reddening. B: baldness. C: mythological beauty.

7. nuque *n.*—A: back of the neck. B: arch of the foot. C: tip of the tongue.

8. hemic *adj.*—A: of the liver. B: of the blood. C: of the stomach.

9. gangling *adj.*—A: infected. B: bunched, as nerves. C: awkwardly tall and thin.

10. cerumen *n.*—A: type of leg brace. B: essential protein. C: earwax.

11. pollex *n.*—A: kneecap or the tissue surrounding it. B: thumb. C: bridge between the nostrils.

12. ventral *adj.*—A: around the stomach. B: leaving the body, as exhaled air. C: fully developed, as a muscle.

13. axilla *n.*—A: network of nerves along the spine. B: long bone of the leg. C: armpit.

14. ossicles *n.*—A: small bones in the ear. B: nerves attached to the eye. C: eyelashes.

15. fontanel *n.*—A: bone in the finger. B: lower-back muscle. C: soft spot in a young skull.

CROSSWORD Upbeat

ACROSS
1 Submissive
5 Jellied garnish
10 Volkswagen Karmann ___
14 "___ Know": Garfunkel
15 *Aida* premiere city
16 Preoccupied
17 Pirate flag
19 Basilica end
20 Sentiments
21 Depress
23 "... riddle me, riddle me ___"
24 Heading of 112.5°
25 Aquarium fish
26 Ernie of golf
27 Manolete, e.g.
30 Like UFC fighters
33 Apollo's birthplace
34 Subsist
35 *Dies* ___ (Latin hymn)
36 *Brady Bunch* girl
37 Does Easter eggs
38 Mr. Potato Head, e.g.
39 ___ nova
40 Affect strangely
41 Access
43 Ex-Dodger Ron
44 Some reunion attendees
45 Paul McCartney, to Stella
46 Shania Twain hit
49 Acrimony
51 Beget
53 Paradise lost
54 Franz Lehàr operetta (with *The*)
56 Sniffer
57 "Excellent!"
58 Number of Beethoven symphonies
59 Consumed
60 Oceanus, e.g.
61 ___ Scott decision

DOWN
1 "Hot Lips" Houlihan's rank
2 Abscond
3 "Da Do Ron Ron" songwriter Greenwich
4 Artisan's furnace
5 "___ the Wide Missouri"
6 A river at Lyon
7 *Animal Farm* beasts
8 High dudgeon
9 Ribbed fabric
10 Dad's dad
11 Henry Winkler series
12 ___ dixit
13 Solar disk
18 Bond number
22 *2001* characters
25 *A Woman Called* ___ (1982)
26 Extra-wide shoe width
27 Jittery
28 Sandwich cookie
29 Relaxation
30 Abduce
31 Eisenberg of Nog fame
32 *Honor Thy Father* author
33 Brake components
36 Disdain
37 Bengals mascot Who ___
39 Court seat
40 Lightly moisten
42 Bankrupt
43 A river runs through it
45 Kishke
46 Lowest point
47 Reconcile
48 Chopped down
49 Remote button
50 Excitements
51 Gumption
52 Peel
55 Assam silkworm

BRAINSNACK® Color It

Which paint (1-3) was used the least to color in the three shapes?

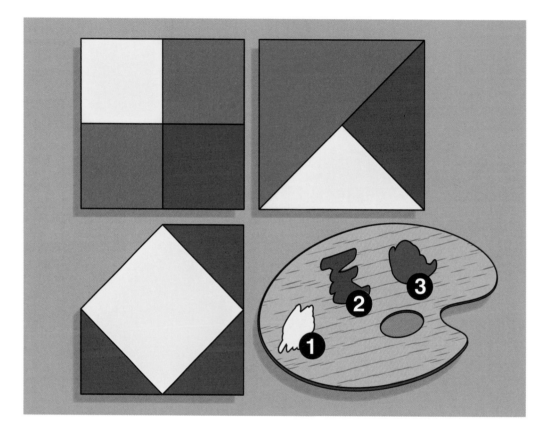

LETTER LINE

Put a letter in each of the squares below to make a word that means "removal from danger."

These numbered clues refer to other words that can be made from the whole:

10 9 2 8 4 1 BEGINNER; 6 4 5 7 1 SHARP;
7 5 10 3 FISH; 4 6 2 1 EARLY DWELLING PLACE.

1	2	3	4	5	6	7	8	9	10

Sudoku X

Fill in the grid so that each row, each column and each 3 x 3 frame contains every number from 1 to 9. The two main diagonals of the grid also contain every number from 1 to 9.

8	6			1	4	2	3	7
						1	6	4
		1						5
	3			6				
		6	1	2	7	5		
7				9	5		4	
		4	7				5	9
		3		4	2			1
				9				

do you KNOW?

What does liqueur Cointreau taste of?

_____

_____

SANDWICH

What four-letter word belongs between the word at left and the word at right, so that the first and second word, and the second and third word, each form a common compound word or phrase?

FLAT _ _ _ _ SIDE

State Flags #1

ACROSS

1 Lopes along
5 Apple attachments
10 Footprint
14 "... pretty maids all in ___ "
15 Pet annoyance
16 Colombia neighbor
17 State with a bear on its flag
19 *Law & Order: Special Victims* ___
20 Flag for all 50 states
21 "Green" superhero
23 Arthur in *Maude*
24 " ___ Day Now": Bob Dylan
25 *All That Jazz* choreographer
26 Roman goddess of plenty
27 Bruised
28 Song from *Mamma Mia!*
31 Pinochle combos
34 "!@#$%," in comics
35 ___-Pitch softball
36 Yankee with over 500 home runs
37 Chop
38 Lily pad, e.g.
39 Early Beatle Sutcliffe
40 Ziegfeld production
41 Saint Catherine's city
42 Sardine whale
43 Radar spot
44 *Jersey Shore* network
45 Ability
47 "Maggie ___": Beatles
48 Charlottesville college
51 Songlike
53 Aquatic turtle
55 Vessel
56 State with a president on its flag
58 Court seat

59 Spread sunshine
60 Function
61 *The Joy Luck Club* nanny
62 Miami golf resort
63 Duck genus

DOWN

1 Ebenezer's partner
2 Vatican cape
3 Israel's Meir
4 Guzzle
5 Cereal utensils
6 Novelist McMillan
7 Counting-out word
8 1,006 in old Rome
9 Hippocampus
10 2007 NBA champs

11 State with three stars on its flag
12 Toledo's lake
13 Green stroke
18 Envelope features
22 Douay Bible book
25 "May the ___ be with you!"
26 Strange
27 Crack of dawn
29 Jones in *American Virgin*
30 Couch
31 Catholic service
32 "*Pas de Deux*" artist
33 State with four pelicans on its flag
34 ACLU part
37 Relaxed (with "out")

38 *Armageddon* actress Tyler
40 Pete Rose's 1,314
41 Harsh
44 Hemingway in *Superman IV*
46 Walter Matthau film
47 Conductor Zubin
48 *Dragon's Teeth* author Sinclair
49 String-quartet member
50 Heche and Rice
51 "Fernando" singers
52 Traipse
53 Nicholas II, e.g.
54 Pearl Mosque site
57 Juan's phone greeting

Keep Going

Start on a blank square of your choice and connect as many blank squares as possible with one single continuous line. You can only connect squares along vertical and horizontal lines, not along diagonal lines. You must continue the connecting line up until the next obstacle, i.e., the rim of the box, a black square or a square that has already been used. You can change direction at any obstacle you meet. Each square can only be used once. The number of blank squares that will be left unused is marked in the upper square. There is more than one solution. We only show one solution.

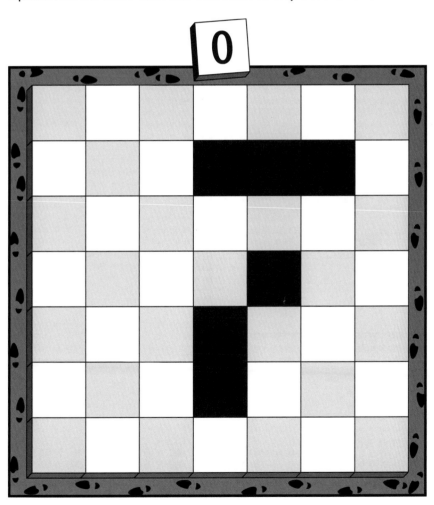

delete ONE

Delete one letter from

ARCTIC EXPEDITION

and rearrange the rest to what could be a travel agent's description.

Cage the Animals

Draw lines to completely divide up the grid into small squares with exactly one animal per square. The squares should not overlap.

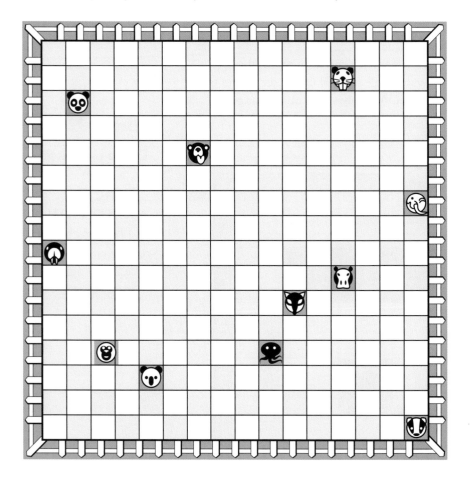

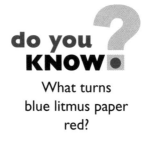

do you **KNOW**

What turns blue litmus paper red?

_____

_____

LETTERBLOCKS

Move the letterblocks around so that words are formed on top and below that you would associate with playing. One block from the top row has been switched to the bottom row.

CROSSWORD Earth Day

ACROSS

1 Type of cherry
5 ___ up trash to celebrate Earth Day
9 Unleaded ___ is cleaner than diesel
12 Imitator
13 A mixture
14 Cheer at the Olympics
15 Dorothy's dog
16 Many ___ can be recycled
18 Head covers
20 Another slang word for copters
21 Cranky
24 Actor Ned or Warren
25 ___ and soul
26 Children's card game
27 ___ -Dick
28 "You ___ me at hello"
29 Unusual
33 ___ feet under
34 Danger
35 Tweets
39 Lizards
40 Recluse
41 Feel bad for
42 Metal that is often recycled
44 Large African country
48 Printer's errors (abbrev.)
49 Average (slang)
50 Puppy ___
51 NNW's opposite
52 Plant a ___ to celebrate Earth Day
53 Mother sheep

DOWN

1 Flying mammal
2 Stock market (abbrev.)
3 What a tightrope walker should have
4 Use reusable ___ bags over paper or plastic
5 Flower featured in The Wizard of Oz
6 Mistakes
7 Spy agency (abbrev.)
8 Like some pickles
9 Innocence's opposite
10 Type of tie
11 Impudent
17 Hot or iced drink
19 Singer Garfunkel
21 Electrical unit
22 ___ Speedwagon
23 Catch
24 Awful
26 Candle substance
28 ___ and hers towels
29 Reduce, reuse, ___
30 Noah's ship
31 ___ de Janeiro
32 Golfer Ernie
33 Short race
34 Dog or cat
35 Applauds
36 Openings
37 Engaged (2 words)
38 Man on the Moon band
39 Child's selfish word
41 Untainted
43 Neither's partner
45 ___ the West Was Won
46 St., Rd., or...
47 ___ Moines, Iowa

Bee's-Eye View

Here's a chance to show how well you can spot and match patterns. How many times can you find the sequence in the large pattern? The sequence may be rotated but not reflected.

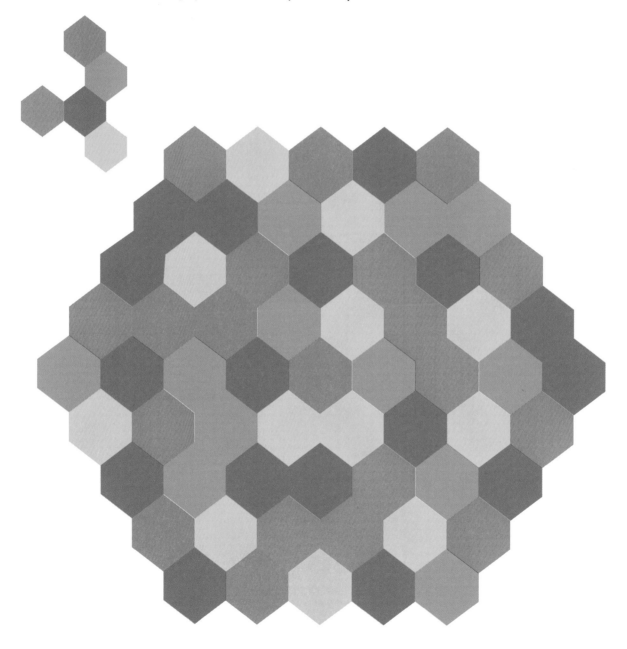

Binairo

Complete the grid with zeros and ones until there are 5 zeros and 6 ones in every row and every column. No more than two of the same number can be next to or under each other. Rows or columns with exactly the same content are not allowed. There is only one valid solution.

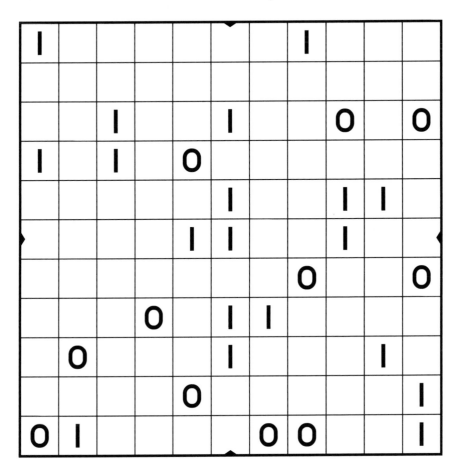

do you KNOW

What country Zug is in?

_____

_____

Low Points

ACROSS

1 "Guys only" party
5 B-complex acid
10 Panache
14 Rose in a *Music Man* song
15 False wing
16 Yoda's pupil
17 *From Here to Eternity* island
18 Of an arm bone
19 *Idomeneo* heroine
20 What Evel Knievel dreamed of making
23 South Carolina river
24 Michele of *Glee*
25 PC ports
27 Little ___ (Custer's last stand)
31 Dot in the ocean
34 Harry Potter, for one
36 New Guinea port
37 TV show hosted by Ronald Reagan
41 Major record label
42 Fast-shrinking sea
43 Icicle sites
44 Aaron's rod, at one point
47 Algerian seaport
49 "32 Flavors" singer DiFranco
50 *Dr. No* star Andress
54 Martian canyon
60 Wicked
61 Acting coach Uta
62 Wrinkly tangelo
63 A flatfish
64 Puff up
65 Ward in *The Fugitive*
66 Dweeb
67 Braved the odds
68 Genesis creation

DOWN

1 Arduous travels
2 Wonder Woman's crown
3 Islamic call to prayer
4 Dress glove
5 Spigot
6 Cantina stew
7 Sally ___ bread
8 "Now ___ me down ..."
9 Wozniacki of tennis
10 *Deep Impact* star Wood
11 Tubby's cartoon chum
12 Tamiroff in *Lord Jim*
13 Lowest high tide
21 3-D feature
22 Not pos.
26 Begin
27 Maria in *Coyote Ugly*
28 Fifth king of Norway
29 Collin of Nashville
30 Capone's nemesis
31 "Beware the ___ of March!"
32 Star-dotted
33 Dragon's den
35 Guido's high note
38 Dropped off the radar
39 Ache
40 Ballerina
45 Bed of straw
46 Opposite of WSW
48 Bankrupt
51 Egged on
52 Charles de Gaulle's birthplace
53 Afghan or Thai, e.g.
54 Sleeveless wear
55 Asseverate
56 Von Shtupp in *Blazing Saddles*
57 ___ fide (in bad faith)
58 Petri-dish gel
59 Fibrous network

Sudoku

Fill in the grid so that each row, each column and each 3 x 3 frame contains every number from 1 to 9.

	7	8		2		6		9
	9						1	5
2		1		5				
			7	3	4			6
8		3			2	7		
7				6			5	2
	8		1	9	3			
	3		2	7				

do you KNOW?

Which Janet had a 1990 Number 1 with "Escapade"?

_____

_____

FRIENDS

What do the following words have in common?

**FORE CALM COME DECK FRIEND GRUDGE
MOAN LITTLE SIDE**

_____

Chill Out

All the words are hidden vertically, horizontally or diagonally—
in both directions.

```
Y U F P C A R I R Q A C G G M W U Q Y
A E J G A J M O Y S D U Y P I S E F Y
I V K S G W O V P R O T R V S G V L E
R C Q Y H T U O U E S J R A T C G U L
C G J U B O L Y M D U V S U E C N I C
O A N E X F R F B A N R D R R I I D I
N L E I P H S T Z N S K G A C M D S S
D R A I L L R W S O C I I E D B A B P
I V L J H L D S O M R N C R B B W O O
T F Q M U R I W W E E R Y E T U K Q P
I Y R N E D P R I L E Z V L M H S P K
O G H T W F C P G A N C U K D E T A K
N H A H P O I M M A N A D N A B W N W
E W M W T D M B Q P G V C I L E I C M
R E W T M T S H I R T P N R U S M E A
B K O O M N O Q Y N S K A P C E W R V
T N V Z V T Z V Y T T B F S G E B Y B
W I H L O O P M I W S X Z K U R D Y K
E A W T L K D R T D G J Y U D T B F K
```

- AIR CONDITIONER
- GRILLING
- POOL
- SUNSCREEN
- BANDANA
- ICE CREAM
- POPSICLE
- SWIM
- COTTON
- LEMONADE
- RAIN
- TREES
- FAN
- MISTER
- ROOT BEER
- T-SHIRT
- FLIP-FLOPS
- MOVIE
- SHORTS
- WADING
- FLUIDS
- NAP
- SPRINKLER
- WATER

BRAINSNACK® Power Panels

All these solar panels generate the same amount of energy. The black squares are damaged solar cells and result in reduced energy. How much energy will the last solar panel generate?

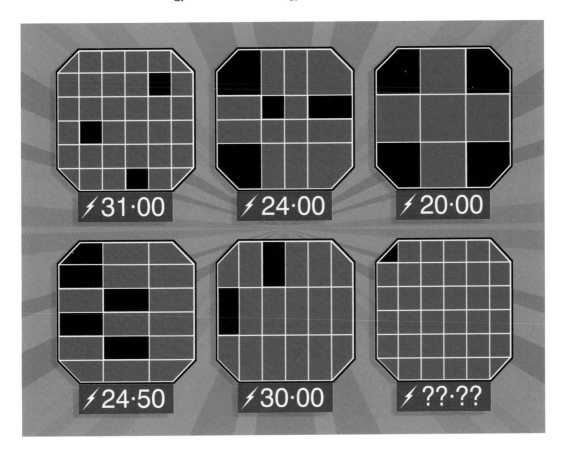

DOODLE PUZZLE

A doodle puzzle is a combination of images, letters and/or numbers that represent a word or a concept. If you cannot solve a doodle puzzle, do not look at the answer right away. Think hard—and outside the box.

RE
RE

Word Sudoku

Complete the grid so that each row, each column and each 3 x 3 frame contains the nine letters from the black box below. The hidden nine-letter word is in the diagonal from top left to bottom right.

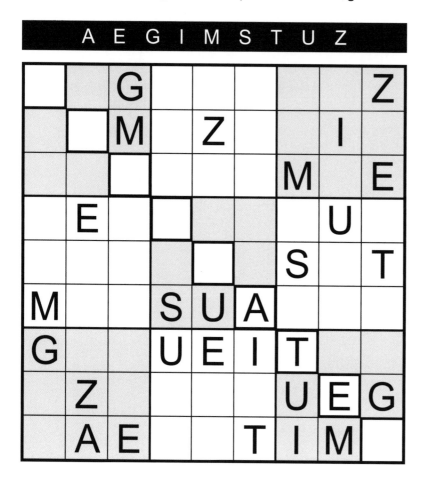

A E G I M S T U Z

TRANSADDITION

Add one letter to **TRAIL NUTS** and rearrange the rest to find a connection.

CROSSWORD # High Points

ACROSS

1 *Do the Right Thing* pizzeria
5 Sandbar
10 Annual melt
14 Hic, ___, hoc
15 "California, ___ come ..."
16 McGowan of *Charmed*
17 Commedia dell'___
18 Windows font
19 Utah resort
20 Highest peak in New Hampshire
23 Break open
24 Polynesian dish
25 City on the Ural
27 Ripped off
31 Skimp
34 Sarah Brightman album
36 Battery size
37 Colorado gold rush slogan
41 *Fables in Slang* author
42 Feminine noun suffix
43 "___ My Head": Ashlee Simpson
44 Use a ruler
47 Hot tubs
49 Sounds from 47 Across
50 Abrade
54 Cut and run
60 *Camelot* character
61 "Oh, ___ don't!"
62 Faculty head
63 Glittering vein
64 "Plant ___ and watch it grow"
65 *High Road to China* heroine
66 Strategy
67 Will Rogers prop
68 TVs

DOWN

1 SeaWorld orca
2 Composer Copland
3 ___ *Now Praise Famous Men*
4 Broadway opener
5 Garments for granny
6 Olympus queen
7 Troublemaking goddess
8 Jacob's first wife
9 Manila man
10 Calamitous
11 Laura of *Remington Steele*
12 Referring to
13 Start on solids
21 Baker's dozen?
22 Persona ___ grata
26 *Nancy Drew* author
27 Chinese lap dogs
28 ___ monde (high society)
29 Sunrise locale
30 *Enterprise* android
31 Cyber junk mail
32 Bay of Fundy attraction
33 Home-furnishings chain
35 Aykroyd in *Ghostbusters*
38 Confidential
39 "La Cucaracha" subject
40 Greyhound trips
45 Bring down
46 "Weird Al" Yankovic movie
48 Bogus
51 An analgesic
52 Braid
53 Anglo-Saxon laborers
54 Beatles album
55 Hydroxyl compound
56 "Another Pyramid" musical
57 "Horse Fair" painter Bonheur
58 Mast chains
59 Attacks weeds

Best in Show

ACROSS

1 Ornery one
5 Impede
10 Cool guys
14 However, to texters
15 "Tag! ___ it!"
16 Hawaiian gala
17 2002 Westminster Best in Show winner
20 Filofax
21 Natives
22 European finch
23 "Can't Help Lovin' ___ Man"
24 One not yet a marquis
27 Spotted wildcats
31 Tiny amounts
34 Hubbub
36 2011 animated film
37 2010 Westminster Best in Show winner
40 Glen ___ Scotch
41 Iron shortage
42 Bridge side
43 More shabby
45 ___-raspberry juice
47 Certain trophy
48 Holiday numbers
52 Nappies
56 Stay longer than
58 2007 Westminster Best in Show winner
60 "Like ___ I go to find my fawn": Shak.
61 McAfee target
62 Hence
63 Cat with ear tufts
64 Pakistani coin
65 Like Frost's woods

DOWN

1 Freebies
2 Helpful
3 *Titanic* finder
4 Glossy to the max
5 Computer storage unit
6 Sullen look
7 ___ *Man in Havana*: Greene
8 Algonquin language
9 Didn't toss
10 Like some cell growth
11 Assembly rooms
12 Baby powder
13 Hauls into court
18 *Black Beauty* writer Sewell
19 Worrywart's words
25 Lorelei's river
26 Ne'er-do-well
27 Pertaining to vision
28 Prove innocent
29 Rail supports
30 Ilk
31 General ___ chicken
32 Four roods
33 Twelve-sided figure
35 Elec. unit
38 Chiang Kai-shek's capital
39 Celebrated
44 Two-family dwelling
46 Prefix for freeze
49 Tidal bore
50 Sovereign
51 Barber's leather
52 Business arrangement
53 Snowboarding stunt
54 Reply
55 Actor LaBeouf
56 Work with a number
57 Heavenly bear
59 ___ Lanka

Sport Maze

Draw the shortest way from the ball to the goal. You can only move along vertical and horizontal lines, not along diagonal lines. The figure on each square indicates the number of squares the ball must be moved in the same direction. You can change direction at each stop.

4	5	5	1	4	4
3	3	2	3	4	5
2	3	1	3	4	5
4	1	0	0	●	4
4	3	2	3	3	5
3	5	3	4	5	2

change ONE

Change one letter in each of these two words to form a common two-word phrase.

TEA CHARGE

ONE LETTER LESS OR MORE

The word on the right side contains the letters of the word on the left side plus or minus the letter in the middle. One letter is already in the right place.

E A R P H O N E +C ☐ ☐ P ☐ ☐ ☐ ☐ ☐

Binairo

Complete the grid with zeros and ones until there are 5 zeros and 6 ones in every row and every column. No more than two of the same number can be next to or under each other. Rows or columns with exactly the same content are not allowed. There is only one valid solution.

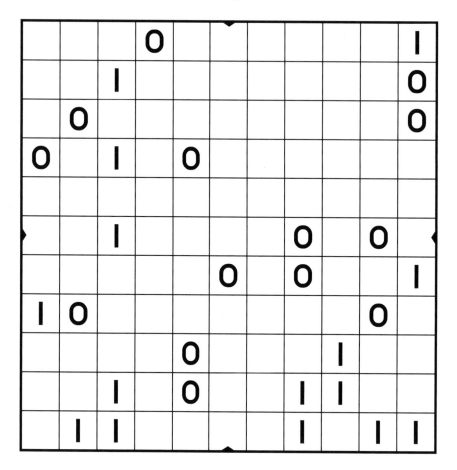

do you KNOW?

Who commanded the Allied forces on D-Day?

_____

_____

REPOSITION PREPOSITION

Unscramble **GO IN TOW** and find a two-word preposition.

BRAINSNACK® Way Out

A driver is making his way across town (see the red route). Can you tell, from
the route he has already taken, where he will leave the map (points A–K)?

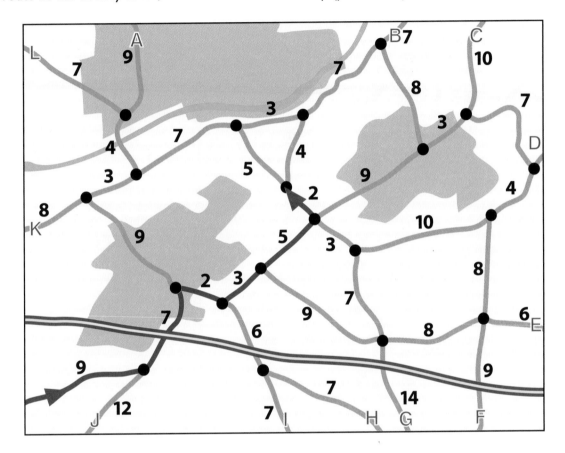

BLOCK ANAGRAM

Form the words that are described in the brackets with the letters above the grid.
Extra letters are already in the right place.

Chocolates (instructor)

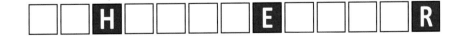

| | | H | | | | E | | | | R |

Sunny

Where will the sun shine, if each arrow points in the direction of a spot where the symbol is located? The symbols cannot be next to each other vertically, horizontally or diagonally. A symbol cannot be placed on top of an arrow. We show one symbol.

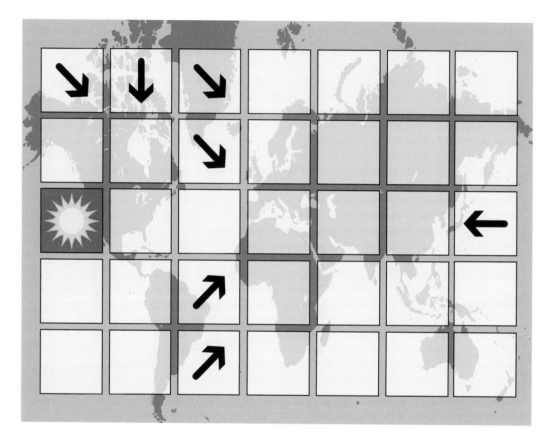

BLOCK ANAGRAM

Form the words that are described in the brackets with the letters above the grid. Extra letters are already in the right place.

POOL TABLE FLY (athlete)

TRIVIA QUIZ **Rosie the Riveter**

By 1944 an unprecedented number of women went to work.
How much do you know about the changes that were underfoot?

1. In 1944, war production represented what percent of the gross national product?

2. The Rosie the Riveter painting originally graced the cover of what magazine?

3. What's angelic about the portrait of Rosie that ran on the magazine cover?

4. At the height of World War II, about what percentage of the 100,000-person Richmond Kaiser shipyard workforce were women?

5. Where is the Rosie the Riveter National Historical Park located?

6. What was the name of the nation's first HMO, originally founded to keep California shipyard workers healthy?

7. What was Atchison Village?

8. Whose painting of Rosie the Riveter was auctioned by Sotheby's on May 22, 2002, for $4,959,500?

TEST YOUR RECALL

Cigarette ads began their long goodbye in 1969 when the National Association of Broadcasters officially endorsed a phaseout. You may be surprised at how many of those long-gone slogans linger in your brain. Match the words to the product.

1. Come to where the flavor is.
2. A silly millimeter longer.
3. You've come a long way, baby.
4. _____ smokers would rather fight than switch!
5. _____ tastes good like a cigarette should.
6. More taste...fine tobacco.
7. I'd walk a mile for a _____.

A. Tareyton
B. Marlboro
C. Camel
D. Kent
E. Virginia Slims
F. Winston
G. Chesterfield 101s

Sudoku

Fill in the grid so that each row, each column and each 3 x 3 frame contains every number from 1 to 9.

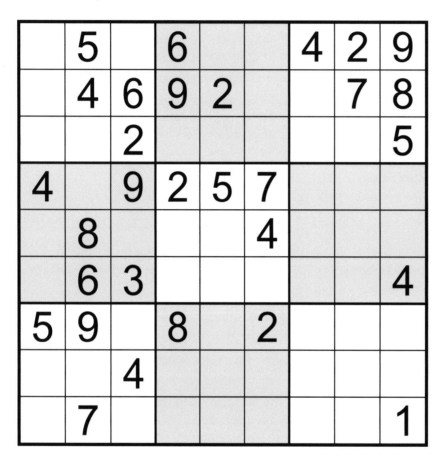

triVia

- Bandleader and singer Louis Armstrong was jazz's foremost virtuoso on which instrument?

FRIENDS

What do the following words have in common?

**COMMITTEE CONSCIOUS CONTRACT CULTURE
DIVIDED HEADING TRACT**

BRAINSNACK® Skewered

A sausage costs half as much as a meatball and a beef cube costs twice as much as a meatball. The entire package costs $16.20. How much does a sausage cost?

DOODLE PUZZLE

A doodle puzzle is a combination of images, letters and/or numbers that represent a word or a concept. If you cannot solve a doodle puzzle, do not look at the answer right away. Think hard—and outside the box.

UCE

Peanuts #2

ACROSS

1 Mayflower pole
5 Jennifer Saunders sitcom
10 "1,000 Oceans" singer Tori
14 Woody Guthrie's son
15 Miss USA prize
16 "... in the pot, ___ days old"
17 Ponytailed pal of Lucy Van Pelt
19 1914 Belgian battle line
20 Tank top's lack
21 Kurtz in *Reality Bites*
23 Cartoon Chihuahua
24 Pitti Palace river
25 *Victor/Victoria* director Blake
29 Limo type
32 Smudgy
33 Gene Pitney song
35 After boo or yoo
36 Where Pericles reigned
37 *Alice in Wonderland* cat
38 Juilliard deg.
39 Lamprey
40 Dishearten
41 Standpoint
42 Perpetual
44 Accompanies
46 Burst into tears
47 "Aye!" sayer
48 *Arabian Nights* character
51 Book-smart
55 Helgenberger of *CSI*
56 Linus is her "Sweet Babboo"
58 Canal of song
59 AOL letter
60 Former Mrs. Tiger Woods
61 Depilatory cream
62 Postponement
63 Delany of *Desperate Housewives*

DOWN

1 2011 NBA champs
2 Bittersweet coating
3 Blackthorn
4 Grin and bear it
5 Be there
6 Major leagues, slangily
7 Distant
8 River of Turkey
9 David Hasselhoff series
10 "Do I have a volunteer?"
11 Linus' teacher
12 "The ___ Love": Gus Kahn
13 Saharan
18 ___ man jack
22 Odd, in Oban
25 *Teen Wolf Too* actress Chandler
26 Dean
27 "The Cat Next Door" to Snoopy
28 *L.A. Law* Emmy winner
29 Spook
30 Dracula's title
31 Party throwers
34 Suffix for ethyl
37 Couldn't stand
38 Deep crimson
40 "Monopoly" card
41 Use elbow grease
43 *The Dark Knight* actor
45 Adroitly
48 Church corner
49 Romance novelist Adrian
50 Identify
51 *A Chapter on Ears* essayist
52 Joe Hardy's girl
53 Mattress size
54 Sicilian resort
57 Data's android daughter

3

Cage the Animals

Draw lines to completely divide up the grid into small squares with exactly one animal per square. The squares should not overlap.

do you KNOW?

What cheese
shares its name
with an
English gorge?

_____

_____

LETTERBLOCKS

Move the letterblocks around so that words are formed on top and below that you would associate with shapes. Two blocks from the top row have been switched with one block from the bottom row.

Letter Search #1

In the grid below, find all appearances of the letter R, both capital and lowercase, any color. When you are ready, set a stopwatch or note the time. Circle every letter R. Then go back and count how many appear in capital and how many in lowercase. Finally, count how many Rs appear in **red**. Note how long it took you, and see if you can beat your time in the other letter searches.

FOR THIS EXERCISE, YOU'LL NEED:
A pen or pencil • A stopwatch or watch or clock with a second hand

```
K  a  N  M  r  r  N  c  N  m  n  k  A  r  X  c  X  m  x  r  N  a
k  R  n  n  r  k  r  X  B  k  k  M  z  N  r  n  k  r  X  N  Z  N
a  x  m  Z  r  R  r  K  Z  N  X  k  R  X  n  k  k  n  R  a  k  X
x  r  x  n  Z  k  m  X  R  r  Z  c  m  x  r  Z  m  X  Z  r  R
m  Z  c  Z  N  a  Z  n  Z  R  m  N  r  R  M  z  A  Z  m  c  k  R
R  m  z  n  X  r  Z  m  N  K  z  x  N  a  z  R  z  M  r  z  X  r
X  z  N  k  m  M  c  z  Z  r  c  X  R  N  n  z  K  R  a  K  k  n
c  m  z  R  z  k  c  M  N  Z  x  m  z  B  a  x  X  M  R  X  m  m
x  X  N  z  m  r  R  x  A  X  n  z  m  Z  X  N  z  M  n  X  a  X
n  X  A  k  r  n  m  x  R  a  X  R  R  r  m  c  R  n  B  a  k  z
k  x  z  M  Z  k  N  z  m  R  N  X  a  k  r  R  x  r  k  X  r  X
B  Z  r  X  r  K  a  Z  B  z  R  z  N  A  k  M  x  X  c  R  n  A
r  X  n  x  a  R  M  k  k  Z  x  r  X  k  a  c  K  x  R  n  R  z
c  x  z  N  R  x  c  M  m  R  n  z  B  M  x  R  z  n  R  z  x  M
N  R  r  R  z  r  R  n  Z  R  n  m  R  A  a  X  X  r  m  R  n  Z
R  z  R  z  N  z  B  x  R  R  r  Z  x  R  n  X  a  z  m  R  x  n
```

TIME_____   NUMBER OF CAPITAL Rs_____

NUMBER OF LOWERCASE Rs_____   NUMBER OF RED Rs_____

CROSSWORD — Check It Out!

ACROSS

1 Romance, mystery or sci-fi, for example
6 "My country ___ of thee..."
9 Musical notes after Mi
12 Hungry
13 Likely
14 First letters of the alphabet
15 Shouts
16 Library's checkout ___
18 Scream when spotting a mouse
20 Indian social group
21 Library's card ___
25 Selected
26 ___ 'n' Andy
27 Dog food brand
29 8 bits, in computer talk
30 *Glee* Actress Michele
31 Speed competition
35 Beach requirement
36 Oblong
37 Incline
41 Call ___ on the spine of a library book
43 Female
44 Internet service provider
45 A library's ___ notice results in a fine
48 3D book for children (hyphenated)
52 Normal (abbrev.)
53 Type of curve
54 Teddy-bearlike creatures in *Star Wars*
55 Time period
56 Type of music
57 ___ decimal system

DOWN

1 Fella
2 Compass direction (abbrev.)
3 Bears' and Eagles' org.
4 Let go
5 Henry Ford's son
6 Tic-___-toe
7 Stock market abbreviation
8 Type of siding
9 Overweight insult
10 Aids in crime
11 Accumulation of rocky debris
17 Slangy "no"
19 Australian bear
21 Taxi
22 Actress Poehler
23 Young child
24 Astronaut John
28 St. Anthony of ___
31 Brat Pack actor (2 words)
32 Road (abbrev.)
33 Auto
34 Elevated trains, for short
35 Return to ___
37 Cussed
38 "I'm a ___, not a fighter"
39 Last letter of the Greek alphabet
40 Even, in golf
42 Scooter
46 America (abbrev.)
47 Sixth sense
49 Bang
50 Little guitar
51 Singer of "Gangnam Style"

Time

All the words are hidden vertically, horizontally or diagonally—in both directions. The letters that remain unused form a sentence from left to right.

```
T I A P R I L F E B R U A R Y
M T S R I F E C E C O N S I S
W U T E R S R E M O N D A Y O
F E F S E A U N S Y E Q U R E
R S D E B N T T C R R E T A L
I D E N M O U U F O E M O U M
D A E T E N F R T T C A J N Y
A Y S I V S T Y R S E U U A T
Y S E C O N D E I I N G S J I
T H G I N S B A A H T U T T U
H E F O U M R T Y R H S N D Q
I M E N E G E T E A L T O S I
I O N T H N A V N F D I W O T
T E P C R I E L E E H N E E N
D E R I G N H T A N R W U R A
S A F T E R N O O N I R I S D
M T W H A O N D L M I N U T E
E N G N T M T O D A Y F G C H
```

- AFTERNOON
- ANTIQUITY
- APRIL
- AUGUST
- CENTURY
- CURRENT
- DAWN
- EARLIER
- EVENING
- FEBRUARY
- FINAL
- FIRST
- FRIDAY
- FUTURE
- HISTORY
- JANUARY
- JUST NOW
- LATER
- MARCH
- MINUTE
- MONDAY
- MORNING
- NEVER
- NIGHT
- NOVEMBER
- PRESENT
- RECENT
- SECOND
- SEPTEMBER
- SOON
- SUNDAY
- TODAY
- TUESDAY
- WEDNESDAY

Keep Going

Start on a blank square of your choice and connect as many blank squares as possible with one single continuous line. You can only connect squares along vertical and horizontal lines, not along diagonal lines. You must continue the connecting line up until the next obstacle, i.e., the rim of the box, a black square or a square that has already been used. You can change direction at any obstacle you meet. Each square can only be used once. The number of blank squares that will be left unused is marked in the upper square. There is more than one solution. We only show one solution.

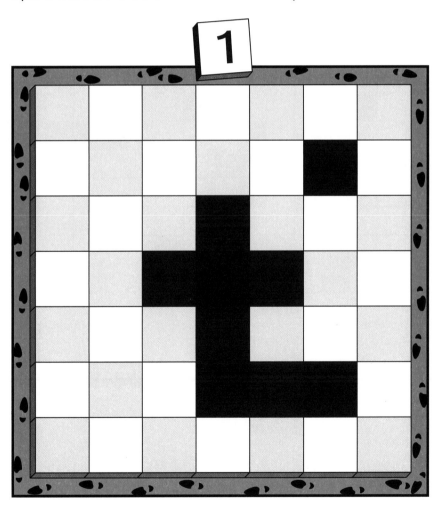

1

delete ONE

Delete one letter from
NEWLY DISAPPEARS
and rearrange the rest to have something to read.

Golden Arches

ACROSS

1 Identical
5 *Caveman* star Ringo
10 *Casablanca* croupier
14 Etel in "The Water Horse"
15 Birchbark
16 Farm component
17 Mickey D's sandwich
19 Aim at the barcode
20 Application filler
21 Boiled
23 *Baywatch* event
24 Mine, to Mimi
25 ___ facto
27 Like potato chips
30 Stage presence
33 Lock of hair
35 New Zealand parrot
36 Aphids
37 New moon, e.g.
38 "Are you for ___?"
39 Application
40 " ___ you ashamed of yourself?"
41 Kunta of *Roots*
42 Buttinski
44 *Messiah* chorus
46 "___ Smile Be Your Umbrella"
47 Blanket or dog
51 Crooked type
54 Augmented fourth
55 "At any ___ ..."
56 Mickey D's breakfast side
58 Politico Romney
59 Enter Colgate
60 "ASAP!"
61 Nautical adverb
62 Gawk
63 Chan's were numbered

DOWN

1 Morley of *60 Minutes*
2 "Drop me ___ sometime"
3 Unfreezes
4 Crunch abs, e.g.
5 Bakery goodies
6 "Dollar Diplomacy" president
7 "32 Flavors" singer DiFranco
8 Friend on *Friends*
9 Drill
10 "For Your Eyes Only" singer
11 Mickey D's sandwich
12 *Deus* ___ (1976 sci-fi novel)
13 Accept an IOU
18 Brown shade
22 120-pound birds
26 Not this
27 Basket in jai alai
28 *Fahrenheit 451* subject
29 "Boola Boola" university
30 "Clue" professor
31 Where the Aisne ends
32 Mickey D's McCafé drink
34 Showed cowardice
37 Delivers a sermon
38 Carnival game
40 Chorus voices
41 Drink from fermented milk
43 Bleep
45 Column stone
48 *Camelot* song "___ Handle a Woman"
49 UN leader (1997–2006)
50 Aviary abodes
51 *Harry Potter* librarian
52 Bushy fox feature
53 *Milk* director Gus Van ___
54 2011 superhero film
57 Malaga Mrs.

Number Cluster

Cubes showing numbers have been placed on the grid below, with some spaces left empty. Can you complete the grid by creating runs of the same number and of the same length as the number? So, where a cube with number 5 has been included on the grid, you need to create a run of five number 5's, including the cube already shown. The run can be horizontal, vertical, or both horizontal and vertical.

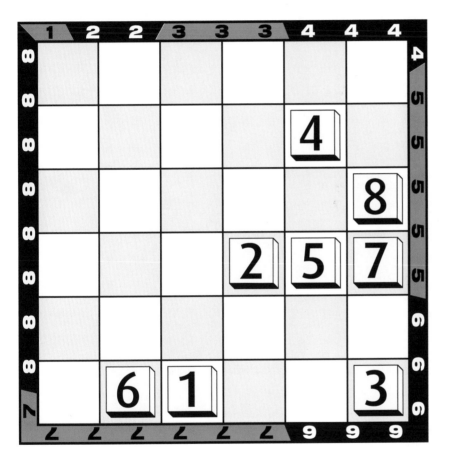

do you KNOW?

What is the name of the largest freshwater lake in the world?

_____

_____

MISSING LETTER PROVERB

Fill in each missing letter, indicated by an X, to make a well-known proverb.

X XATXXED XOX XEVEX XOILX

Spot the Differences

Find the nine differences between the images.

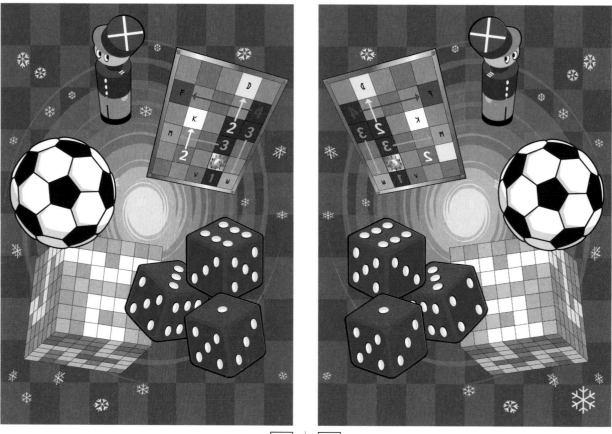

BLOCK ANAGRAM

Form the words that are described in the brackets with the letters above the grid. Extra letters are already in the right place.

Polar sea (photovoltaic)

		L					N	

CROSSWORD Themeless

ACROSS

1 Help with a heist
5 Siesta
10 *Comus* composer
14 Roy Orbison hit
15 "Do I ___ Waltz?"
16 Film spool
17 Mustang parent
18 Canine name
19 "Keeper of sheep" in Genesis
20 "You Are the ___ of My Life"
22 Verbal assault
24 Wild cat
25 Cohen-Chang on *Glee*
26 Pinch pennies
29 Not ready to jump in yet
33 Yet to come
34 U.S. Open winner Safin
35 London lav
36 *Bruce Almighty* star
39 Parrot genus
40 Opus for nine
41 "... ___ of do or die"
42 Metric 2.2 pounds
44 Acted rudely, in a way
45 Politico Gingrich
46 Banana throwaway
47 Pentax product
50 Nonthinking
54 *The Time Machine* slaves
55 Beast of Borneo
57 "Idomeneo" heroine
58 Gave up the ghost
59 Sadness
60 Katz of *Dallas*
61 "Trust in Me" singer James
62 College near Albany
63 Josh Groban Christmas album

DOWN

1 Charity
2 Spark
3 Be a breadwinner
4 Actor
5 "Popcorn" shellfish
6 "I Will Be" singer Lewis
7 Trough locale
8 Before
9 Adherent
10 Noah's landfall
11 "And Still" singer McEntire
12 Must have
13 *Legally Blonde* blonde
21 Lulu
23 Began
25 Monster: Comb. form
26 "Solve or spin" sayer
27 Oteri in *The Ant Bully*
28 Concerning the kidneys
29 Female seal group
30 Church area
31 *Hang 'Em High* prop
32 ___ down (moderated)
34 "Down Under" group ___ Work
37 Soccer positions
38 Green onion
43 Big name in flatware
44 Madam of the casa
46 Attach a nametag
47 Formally surrender
48 Came back down
49 ___ & Chandon
50 1.6 kilometers
51 *Blondie* boy
52 Beget
53 Windmill blade
56 ___ polloi

What's Missing?

Take a look at the sets of images on this spread. Your task is to deduce which of the four options given in each case completes the set.

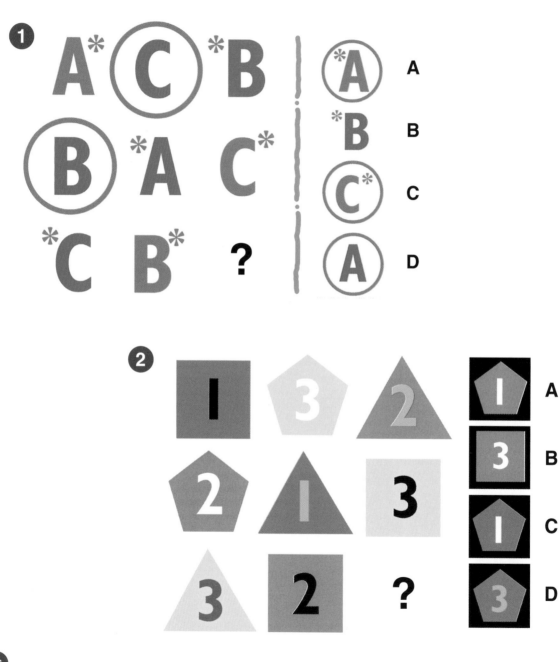

3

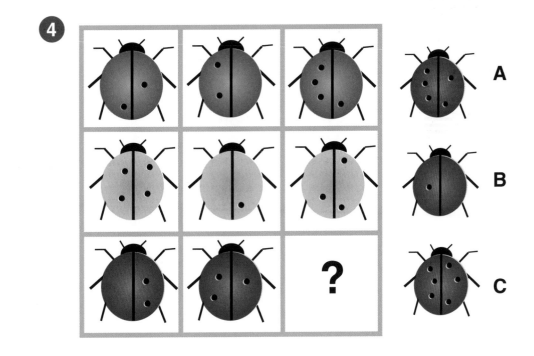

A

B

C

D

4

A

B

C

State Flags #2

ACROSS

1 Upper House member
5 North Dakota's state trees
9 Kathy in "About Schmidt"
14 Iroquois foe
15 Prefix with drome
16 Admits customers
17 "1858" is on this state's flag
19 Ripley's *Believe It ___!*
20 Swear off
21 Nevada's state tree
23 Office neckwear
24 Rip
26 Ripe old age
29 A pop
30 Sommer in *Jenny's War*
32 Notice
33 Stephen ___ King
36 Magnus and McClurg
37 123-45-6789 org.
38 Action-painting technique
39 Young haddock
40 *Fantasia* frames
41 "Classical ___" (1968 hit)
42 Act smitten
43 Pick up the tab
44 Duke's conference
45 1, on the Mohs scale
46 Go for it
47 B&B patron
49 *Felicity* star Russell
51 ___ Wednesday
54 Standards
56 Hall-of-Famer Alomar
58 Anwar's successor
60 Goddess Ceres is on this state's flag
62 Mexican Oscar
63 Sarah McLachlan hit
64 A puck in a net
65 ___ Cristo sandwich

66 Ivy League school
67 "I'm buying!"

DOWN

1 *American Graffiti* actor Paul
2 Veldt antelope
3 "Lather, ___, repeat"
4 Jalopy ding
5 Not so hard
6 "I Will Be" singer Lewis
7 *The A-Team* star
8 *All My Children*, e.g.
9 Backwoods
10 Gordon Ramsay's wear
11 Three stars are on this state's flag

12 Wine prefix
13 Former British Airways jet
18 Polished off
22 Signed a contract
25 Las Vegas resort
27 Silicon Valley car company
28 Leavening
29 *Great Expectations* boy
31 Big cat
33 "*Bust of a Woman*" painter Degas
34 Potter rival Malfoy
35 "1848" is on this state's flag

36 *Earth in the Balance* subject: Abbrev.
39 Locust cloud
40 Shed a tear
42 Antiseptic
43 William & Mary team
46 Computer virus
48 "*Haystacks*" painter
50 "Desert Fox" Rommel
51 Insurance scheme
52 Cook dim sum
53 "According to" rules guy
55 Crisp cookie
57 "And so ..."
58 *Green Eggs and ___*
59 Italian gold
61 Dutch piano center

BRAINSNACK® **Write Me**

Which letter should replace the question mark?

END GAME

The words you are seeking all have the letters END in them in the position indicated.
When you have found all of the answers, with help from the clues on the right, one column will reveal the END GAME word, which is an end game in itself.

__	__	__	__	__	E	N	D	Squander
__	__	E	N	D	__	__	__	Cruel, wicked
__	E	N	D	__	__	__	__	Available as a resource
E	N	D	__	__	__	__	__	Inner layers of cells

Sport Maze

Draw the shortest way from the ball to the goal. You can only move along vertical and horizontal lines, not along diagonal lines. The figure on each square indicates the number of squares the ball must be moved in the same direction. You can change direction at each stop.

1	3	3	1	5	1
2	2	2	3	2	4
3	4	●	3	1	4
5	1	0	2	2	4
5	3	3	3	2	2
4	1	3	4	5	4

change ONE

Change one letter in each of these two words to form a common two-word phrase.

ROT BAKES

ONE LETTER LESS OR MORE

The word on the right side contains the letters of the word on the left side plus or minus the letter in the middle. One letter is already in the right place.

D O M I N A N T +B ☐ ☐ ☐ ☐ I ☐ ☐ ☐ ☐

WORD SEARCH Spring

All the words are hidden vertically, horizontally or diagonally—in both directions. The letters that remain unused form a sentence from left to right.

```
E P V E G E T A B L E S V E N
T H O L A N D S C A P E O U G
S G L L H S F O A L W E H A B
V U T A E C T N A R E B U X E
E B N I T V O E E B F E C P G
O Y M B U E E M R L I E R M I
U A N C E R S D P H L O L E N
M M S E S A F P D O M O E P N
S E N S C D M E R I S G P E I
I N B S E T T S S I N T P T N
M O L P N S A E N I N O C S G
I N O R A T S R N U H G A O R
T O S I E S P A P R I L L C L
P S S N R I E B L N G J F E E
O A O G M L I I S G A K U T A
E E M N C R G S G E N V E N V
R S E Y D H O N G E H U A E E
P W P S T S T N E C S Y S P S
```

- APRIL
- BEGINNING
- BIRDS
- BLOSSOM
- CALF
- CLEANING
- COMPOST
- DEVELOP
- EASTER
- EGGS
- EXUBERANT
- FOAL
- FRUIT
- HOPE
- JUNE
- LANDSCAPE
- LATE SPRING
- LEAVES
- LIFE
- LIGHT
- MAYBUG
- NECTAR
- NEW
- OPTIMISM
- PENTECOST
- POLLEN
- PROMISE
- SCENTS
- SEASON
- SPRING
- SUNBEAMS
- SUNGLASSES
- VEGETABLES

Word Pyramid

Each word in the pyramid has the letters of the word above it, plus a new letter.

F
(1) musical note
(2) plump
(3) quick
(4) realities
(5) workmanships
(6) elements
(7) prediction

do you KNOW?

Which land was
Helen of Troy
queen of?

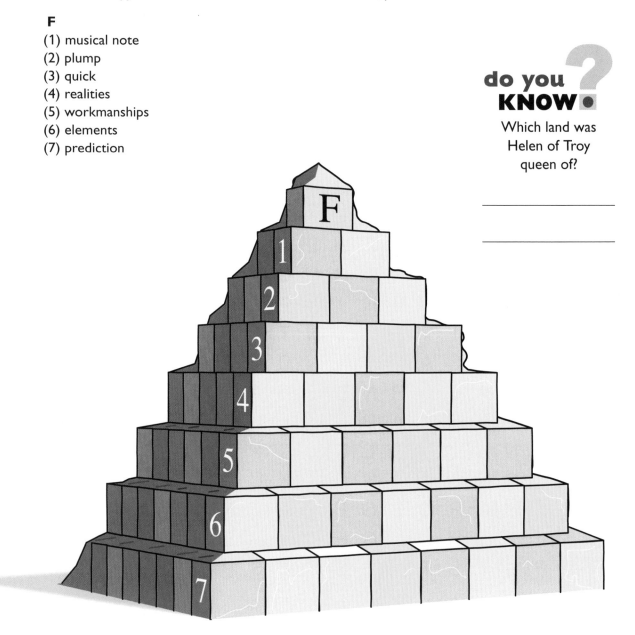

CROSSWORD **State Birds**

ACROSS

1 Big name in cookware
5 German art song
9 "Beat it!"
14 Prefix for drome
15 Green emotion
16 "___ in Paradise": Poe
17 State bird of Maine
19 "The Lovely" Muse
20 Legolas player Bloom
21 Adjective for a model
23 "Fore!" site
24 "Me too" sort
25 Eeyore's creator
29 Agar colony
32 ___ a Letter to My Love (1981)
33 Baseball deal
35 "Go ahead" signal
36 Caribou male
37 Something to get into
38 Tucked away
39 TV type
40 Part of a lunar cycle
41 Crime site
42 Shoreline problem
44 Rap sheets
46 "Not so fast!"
47 Dancer Lubovitch
48 Peach State capital
51 Transcend
55 Authoritative proclamation
56 State bird of New Jersey
58 Sacher cake
59 Dawn author Wiesel
60 A Plains tribe
61 Fahrenheit 451 actor Werner
62 Dog food brand
63 Attacks, puppy-style

DOWN

1 Snack with a shell
2 Oded in The Mummy
3 Nutmeg covering
4 GPS asset
5 Slow and heavy
6 Prefix for China
7 "Who's That Girl" rapper
8 Hides the gray
9 St. Patrick's spire
10 Trumpet look-alike
11 State bird of New Mexico
12 Poker stake
13 "Is it just ___ ..."
18 Genuflected
22 Magna cum ___
25 Usher's beat
26 Daisy relative
27 State bird of Kansas
28 Hawke in Great Expectations
29 Pickled bud
30 Roly-poly
31 A cube has twelve
34 Dorm police, so to speak
37 Piglet
38 Desert stinger
40 Avant-gardist
41 Flying ace Snoopy's wear
43 1999 Jake Busey sitcom
45 Loses a tail
48 Prefix for pilot
49 Ali stats
50 Like single malt Scotch
51 Snowboarded
52 Voting "no"
53 Old English poet
54 "___ a Lady": Tom Jones
57 ABBA drummer Brunkert

The year 1949 was significant in the world of sports and
in many ways ushered in a new era of organized sport as big-money entertainment.
Both the NBA and the LPGA formed that year. And U.S. Open tennis champ
Ricardo "Pancho" Gonzalez turned pro, earning $85,000 in his first six months on tour.

DO YOU RECALL THESE OTHER '49 MILESTONES?

1 This Yankees slugger signed the major league's first $100,000 annual contract.

2 This Original Six NHL team won its third Stanley Cup in a row, a feat it would repeat in '62, '63 and '64. (Hint: The team hasn't won the Cup since 1967.)

3 This boxer retired after a 12-year reign as world heavyweight champ.

4 This team signed its first African-American players, outfielder Monte Irvin and pitcher Ford Smith. Only Irvin played in the majors.

5 This St. Louis Cardinal "hit for the cycle"—a single, double, triple and home run—in a game against Brooklyn that ended in a 14-1 Dodgers loss.

TEST YOUR RECALL

In 1949 what car was chosen as Motor Trend Car of the Year?

Sudoku

Fill in the grid so that each row, each column and each 3 x 3 frame contains every number from 1 to 9.

4						5		
	9	6			2		4	
	1		9	5		7		
				8	1			
	6	9		4		3	8	
			3	2				
		1		3	8		5	
	8		7			2	6	
		2						1

do you KNOW?

Where did the name "Mark Twain" come from?

_____

_____

triVia • The ears of the African elephant can be over 3 feet wide.

Apart from improving the elephant's hearing, what other purpose do they serve?

_____

Comic Book Heroes

ACROSS

1 Race car driver Al
6 Multitude
10 Bruce Banner alter ego
14 Give back
15 Ye ___ Tea Shoppe
16 "___ go bragh!"
17 Get up
18 Marvel *X-Men* character with mutant powers
20 Mother ___
21 Ache
22 Lemon or lime ending
23 Novelist Wharton
27 Takeo ___, Japanese WWII general
28 ___ 9000 from *2001: A Space Odyssey*
29 Blunder
31 Part of a book or table
33 Spanish language chant
35 Political abbreviation
36 '44 Gene Tierney film
38 Bye in Barcelona
42 Queen for ___ (2 wds.)
44 Marvel superheroine aka Ororo Munroe
46 Erase
47 Painter of *Water Lilies*
49 Finished
51 By way of
52 ___ Lanka
54 Shade or tint
55 Fountain pen filler
56 Lid
59 Run ___ course
61 Corrodes
63 Military address (abbrev.)
64 Right away (abbrev.)
66 Small stream
69 Marvel superhero, alter ego of Matt Murdock
72 Forbidden
73 R&B singer James

74 Type of wolf
75 Mrs. Flintstone
76 Marvel superhero; God of thunder
77 Mr. Astaire
78 Mr. T's group (2 wds.)

DOWN

1 Russian mountain range
2 Roman emperor from 54-68 AD
3 Alter ego for Peter Parker
4 Guided gently
5 Type of bread
6 Female pig
7 Horse hoof sound
8 '52 and '56 presidential candidate Stevenson
9 *Taxi* actor Danny
10 *On ___ Majesty's Secret Service*
11 ___ the Hittite
12 California city, with 67 Down
13 Genuflect
19 Bomber ___ Gay
24 Sick
25 Green, black and chai
26 Terre ___, Indiana
29 Type of cheese
30 Make new
32 Line of weather
34 Part of a school's URL
37 Zeal
39 Comic book hero Sue Richards, ___ Woman
40 Father of 76 Across

41 Drench
43 Affirmative
45 Restaurant's list of options
48 Group of three
50 ___ Moines, Iowa
53 "It speaks for ___"
56 Police officer in training
57 "Beat ___ to the door" (2 wds.)
58 2nd largest city in Portugal
60 Enjoy
62 Characteristic
65 An evergreen
67 California city, with 12 Down
68 Rich soil
70 Cob
71 Type of bulb
72 Former airline

Binairo

Complete the grid with zeros and ones until there are 6 zeros and 6 ones in every row and every column. No more than two of the same number can be next to or under each other. Rows or columns with exactly the same content are not allowed. There is only one valid solution.

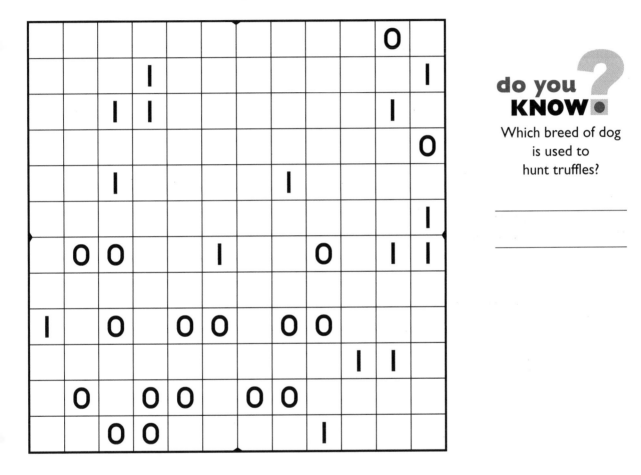

do you KNOW?

Which breed of dog is used to hunt truffles?

_____

_____

REPOSITION PREPOSITION

Unscramble **READ GRASS** and find a two-word preposition.

_____

Cage the Animals

Draw lines to completely divide up the grid into small squares with exactly one animal per square. The squares should not overlap.

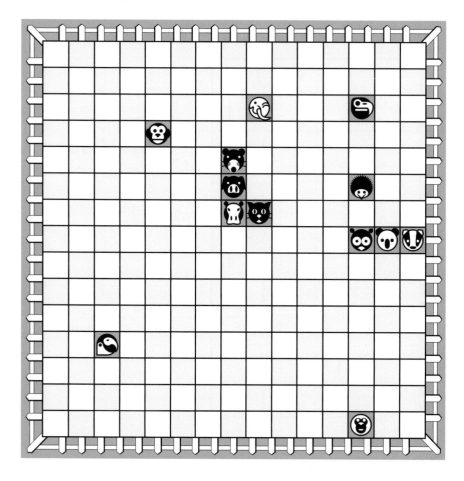

do you KNOW?

Who was the U.S. president before Franklin Roosevelt?

_____

_____

LETTERBLOCKS

Move the letterblocks around so that words are formed on top and below that you can associate with insects.

WORD POWER Animal Instincts

Do you know your budgies from your whippets? Your alpacas from your yaks?
We separate the mice from the men by testing your knowledge of all creatures
great and small. How many of these wild words can you tame?

. . . .

1. ailurophile *n.*—A: lover of cats.
B: one who is afraid of animals.
C: collector of snakes.

2. leporine *adj.*—of or relating to …
A: a parrot. B: a goat. C: a hare.

3. komondor *n.*—A: Hungarian
sheepdog. B: mythical lizard.
C: trained falcon.

4. Komodo dragon *n.*—A: Chinese
miniature dog. B: Indonesian lizard.
C: North American toad.

5. caudal *adj.*—A: having pointed
ears. B: born as twins. C: tail-like.

6. stridulate *v.*—A: shed a coat.
B: mate. C: make a shrill noise by
rubbing together body structures, as a
cricket does.

7. clowder *n.*—A: fish food. B: group
of cats. C: old-fashioned wooden
dog toy.

8. brindled *adj.*—A: streaky, as a
coat. B: vaccinated. C: on end, as
neck hairs.

9. card *v.*—A: breed for docility.
B: brush or disentangle fibers, as of
wool. C: demand to know a dog's
pedigree.

10. zoolatry *v.*—A: animal worship.
B: system for grouping animals.
C: study of animal communication.

11. vibrissa *n.*—A: whisker.
B: horse's hoof. C: tortoise's lower
shell.

12. grimalkin *n.*—A: frog pond.
B: hip injury in dogs. C: old female cat.

13. feral *adj.*—A: rabid or otherwise
diseased. B: pregnant or in heat.
C: not domesticated.

14. cosset *v.*—A: pamper or treat
as a pet. B: selectively breed. C: grow
more docile.

15. ethology *n.*—A: proper
treatment of animals. B: science of
genetics. C: study of animal behavior.

Say Cheese!

ACROSS

1 Act a bit vexed
5 Alop
10 "A" in code
14 " ___ on Down the Road"
15 Office scribe
16 Welsh form of John
17 Smidgen
18 "Great blue" bird
19 Censor's concern
20 Mild cheese with an orange rind
22 Twofold
24 *Pollyanna* author Porter
25 Indira Gandhi's father
26 Book before Exod.
27 Once upon a time
30 Algonquian abode
33 Becomes wan
34 Prizm maker
35 Frau's partner
36 Larry of *Curb Your Enthusiasm*
37 Wall Street animal
38 Orinoco tributary
39 *Dragonwyck* writer Anya
40 A moving crowd
41 Penultimate month
43 "April Love" singer Boone
44 "___ Melancholy": Keats
45 "Could be"
49 Auriferous
51 Spaghetti cheese
52 Mine, in Marseilles
53 16th-century violin
55 Largest Latvian city
56 Unaccompanied
57 Urge forward
58 Major German dam
59 Two-___ sloth
60 Acts like a stallion
61 Rolltop

DOWN

1 "Cherchez la ___!"
2 *High Sierra* director Walsh
3 *Teen Wolf Too* actress Chandler
4 Hannah Montana, for one
5 Kutcher of *Two and a Half Men*
6 Texas longhorn
7 Virginia/North Carolina lake
8 Roxy Music founder
9 Pondered
10 Allay one's fears
11 Odorous German cheese
12 NBA technical
13 "Deal me in" indicator
21 Snicker-___
23 "Law" of current flow
25 *Baywatch* actress Gena
27 Act of goodwill
28 Coveted role
29 Former times
30 "Better you ___ me!"
31 Bubble Chair designer Aarnio
32 Antipasto cheese
33 Eucharist holder
36 Blithe
37 Annoyed
39 Pirate known to the Lost Boys
40 Damage
42 Circulated, in a way
43 Hazards
45 ___ Noster
46 Stage whisper
47 Beeper calls
48 "The Hunting of the ___": Carroll
49 *Atlas Shrugged* hero
50 Herman Melville book
51 Hemingway epithet
54 Spouse of M.

Kakuro

Each number in a black area is the sum of the numbers that you have to enter in the next empty boxes. The empty boxes that make up the sum are called a run. The sum of the across run is written above the diagonal in the black area and the sum of the down run is written below the diagonal in the black area. Runs can only contain the numbers 1 through 9 and each number in a run can only be used once. The gray boxes only contain odd numbers and the white only even numbers.

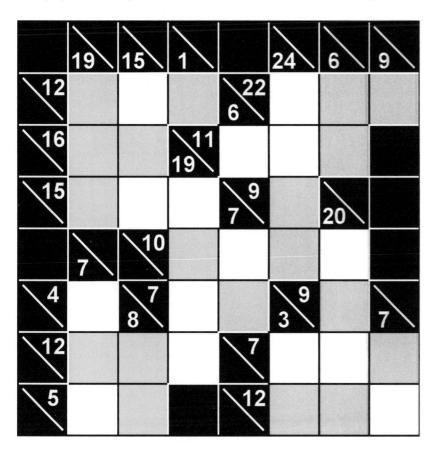

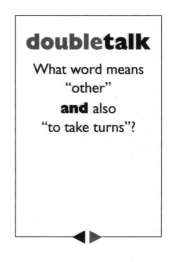

doubletalk

What word means "other" **and** also "to take turns"?

MISSING LETTER PROVERB

Fill in each missing letter, indicated by an X, to make a well-known proverb.

X XIXX IS XX GXXD XX A XILX

Missing Plan

You see all the sides of six cubes. The grid on the right was formed by placing the floor plans of the cubes next to each other. The floor plan of which cube (1–6) is not in the grid?

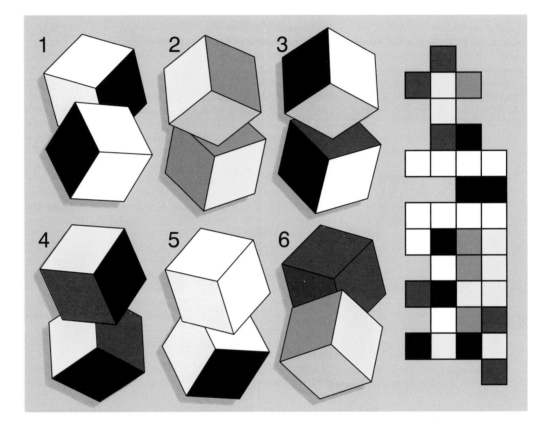

DOODLE PUZZLE

A doodle puzzle is a combination of images, letters and/or numbers that represent a word or a concept. If you cannot solve a doodle puzzle, do not look at the answer right away. Think hard—and outside the box.

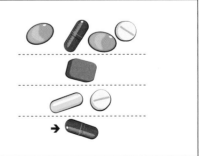

CROSSWORD U.S. Cities

ACROSS

1 Makes public
5 Israeli statesman Dayan
10 Take five
14 Barrymore in *Whip It*
15 At three o'clock, asea
16 Court minutes
17 Prefix meaning "all"
18 *Children of the Sun* playwright
19 Source of fiber
20 Florida's "Sunshine City"
23 Cause for court-ordered rehab
24 Bee prefix
25 Answered
29 Distinguished
33 Survey-answer choice
34 J.D. Salinger heroine
36 A fifth of DX
37 Virginia city named after King George III's wife
41 ___ *for Killer*: Grafton
42 Banana throwaway
43 "___ ears!"
44 Royal emblem
47 Settled
49 Mount where Aaron died
50 Temporary drop
51 U.S. Air Force Academy locale
60 Take too much of
61 He fails to pass the bar
62 Geese that rarely swim
63 Things on other things
64 Kiwi-shaped
65 Ovid's "it was"
66 Darjeeling and Oolong
67 4 x 4, e.g.
68 The i's have it

DOWN

1 Kerfuffles
2 Food maven Rombauer
3 "Labors of Hercules" artist
4 Con artist
5 Chatterbox
6 Hecklephone cousin
7 Spanish muralist
8 Whiting
9 Sheikhdoms
10 White Carroll creature
11 Cream shade
12 Five-pointed figure
13 Grapefruit taste
21 Play with idly
22 Whirlpool setting
25 Ice, in bar lingo
26 Value system
27 Lunar stage
28 Ward off
29 Detect a fragrance
30 Brilliant performance
31 Capital of Nord, France
32 Road sign
35 ___ Anne de Bellevue
38 Jim Croce hit
39 Chapel head
40 Not in reality
45 Telethon bank
46 Rocky top
48 Diving fisher
51 Egyptian Christian
52 Drooling dog of comics
53 *Shark Tale* dragon fish
54 Did a half gainer
55 Judy Moody's aunt
56 Bee bristle
57 Sleuth Wolfe
58 Irritating insect
59 Hardens

Sudoku Twin

Fill in the grid so that each row, each column and each 3 x 3 frame contains every number from 1 to 9. A sudoku twin is two connected 9 x 9 sudokus.

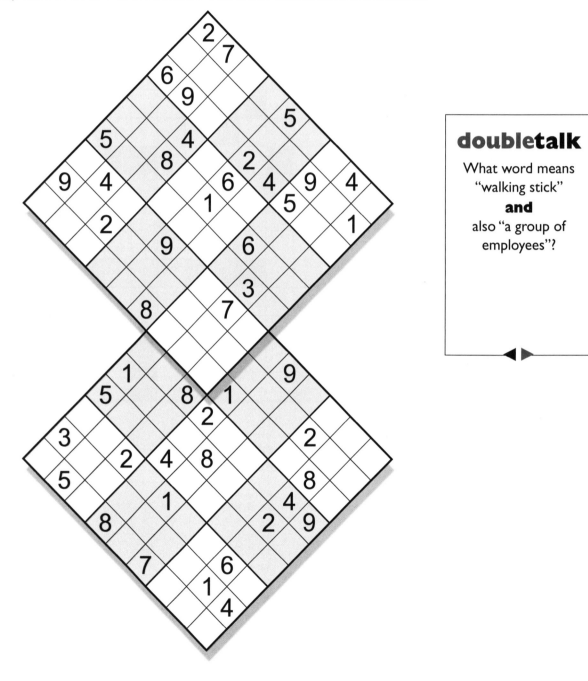

Keep Going

Start on a blank square of your choice and connect as many blank squares as possible with one single continuous line. You can only connect squares along vertical and horizontal lines, not along diagonal lines. You must continue the connecting line up until the next obstacle, i.e., the rim of the box, a black square or a square that has already been used. You can change direction at any obstacle you meet. Each square can only be used once. The number of blank squares that will be left unused is marked in the upper square. There is more than one solution. We only show one solution.

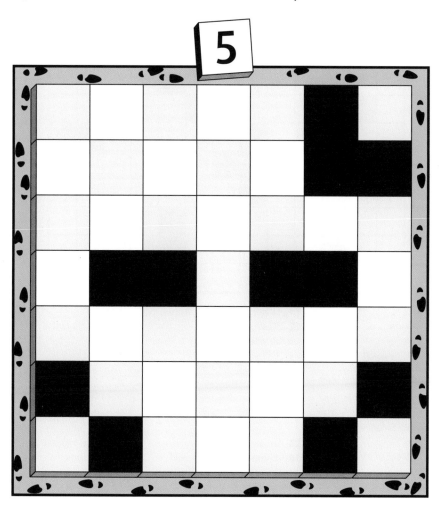

Cinema Classics

ACROSS

1 "Breakdance" singer Irene
5 Sadistic
10 He aims for the heart
14 Penn State mascot
15 "Do I ___ Waltz?"
16 Hawaii's "Valley Isle"
17 Latin 101 verb
18 Improv joke
19 Chorale member
20 Flabby
22 Maine feline
24 Achilles ___
25 Gaseous house hazard
26 Icelandic speakers
28 Announces
30 Sudden outpouring
32 Ananias and Matilda
34 Extinct relative of 37-Across
35 *Dies* ___ ("Judgment Day")
36 Phone messages
37 120-pound Australians
38 "Glue" for feathers
39 "___ Eclipse of the Heart"
40 Accords
41 Purchase
43 Dig discovery
45 Audio signal receiver
46 "Dover Beach" poet
49 Leslie in *Mr. Magoo*
51 Like pacifists
52 Prefix meaning "eight"
53 *Titanic* room
55 Hawaii's state bird
56 *Enterprise* android
57 Pageant crown
58 Happy flower?
59 Musher's transport
60 Price for clearance
61 Dove into home

DOWN

1 Chin dimple
2 Passageway
3 *Desperately Seeking Susan* star
4 Raconteur's offering
5 Jacob Marley's burden
6 Foxx in *Sanford and Son*
7 "Friendly Skies" airline: Abbrev.
8 Stonestreet of *Modern Family*
9 Hands
10 Mr. Spock's mother
11 *A Clockwork Orange* star
12 Utter
13 Warden's worry
21 It's melted in a meltdown
23 Regatta athletes
27 Be heart-pleasing
28 "From the ___ of Montezuma ..."
29 "Yo mama," e.g.
30 "Come in and ___ spell"
31 Kind of joke
33 Dockworkers' union
36 Rectifies
37 Annual report data
39 Father's Day gifts
40 Component
42 Pawn off
44 Disney's Montana
47 Maui neighbor
48 Judge played by Stallone
49 Auction bids
50 Catch red-handed
51 Affectations
54 Ovine sound

WORD SEARCH France

All the words are hidden vertically, horizontally or diagonally—in both directions. The letters that remain unused form a sentence from left to right.

```
W I T H D N R E N N E S V I V
E R L S O E D I P S H S O E S
B N I Y M I C H E L I N S C S
R A L P S D U C T R H N G A M
I N L A S R B O A U I O E S A
E C E P I A F P N L L N S T R
A Y B A I T S S Q E A G N L S
P Y R E N E E S U S E I N E E
F R E N C H B R E A D V N S I
D E O C A S E S O A L A A U L
C N L V E T F C Z Y A R P E L
N A C H E C U N I D V I O P E
G U N S R N A W I N E I L A N
A L E G I V C X C A N N E S I
R T S K O N O E W M D N O T A
L N D U L C L L O R E V N I E
I D R A L L O O V O R E R S T
C H E B O U R S I N W O R L D
```

- ALPS
- AVIGNON
- AZNAVOUR
- BOURSIN
- BRIE
- CANNES
- CASTLES
- COGNAC
- FRENCH BREAD
- GARLIC
- LAVENDER
- LILLE
- LOIRE
- LYON
- MARSEILLE
- MICHELIN
- NANCY
- NAPOLEON
- NICE
- NORMANDY
- PARIS
- PASTIS
- PETANQUE
- PIAF
- PROVENCE
- PYRENEES
- RENAULT
- RENNES
- SEINE
- SOLEX
- TARDI
- VOSGES
- WINE

BRAINSNACK® Ice Melt

As the inclination of the earth increases compared to the sun, more ice melts on the polar caps. How many thousands of cubic kilometers of ice will melt if the inclination is 18°?

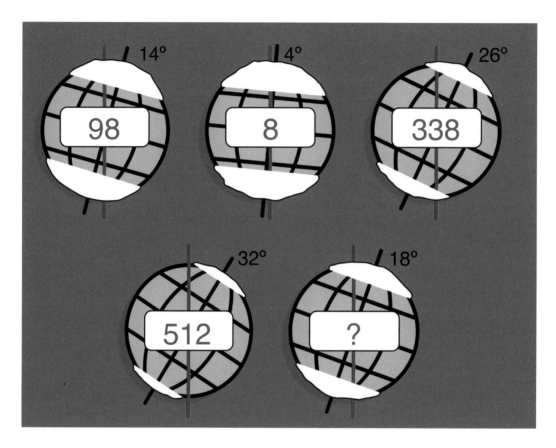

DOODLE PUZZLE

A doodle puzzle is a combination of images, letters and/or numbers that represent a word or a concept. If you cannot solve a doodle puzzle, do not look at the answer right away. Think hard—and outside the box.

WORK

CROSSWORD **Themeless**

ACROSS

1 "Isn't that ___ much?"
5 Baron Cohen in *Borat*
10 A sound from the tower
14 All dried out
15 iPad letters
16 Jamaican tangelo
17 Stravinsky ballet
18 Twenty, in Paris
19 "Heads I win, tails you ___"
20 *Fear and Loathing in Las Vegas* author
23 Arched shoe parts
24 Spicy tea
25 Green lights
26 Rather brief
30 Swiss capital
33 They come in drops
34 Greene of *The Godfather*
35 Indonesia's ___ Islands
36 "Bon appétit!"
37 Southern California valley
38 Country singer McGraw
39 Better balanced
40 It runs in a taxi
41 Beyond gaunt
43 Hawaii's Mauna ___
44 Horse for Lawrence
45 Airborne weapon
49 1956 Elvis Presley hit
53 "___ Breaky Heart"
54 *Fantastic Voyage* carrier
55 *Avatar* humanoids
56 "Long-running" suffix
57 Deli cheese
58 Tavern tipples
59 Hades river
60 Ho-hum feeling
61 Folk knowledge

DOWN

1 Japanese brewery
2 "We've Only Just ___"
3 Jeremy in *Betrayal*
4 12:50
5 French porcelain
6 Off-kilter
7 "Got other plans, sorry"
8 Seat with a tray
9 Valved brass instrument
10 Jack-in-the-___
11 Big heads
12 To boot
13 Creditor's claim
21 Sommer in *A Shot in the Dark*
22 Father of Remus
26 Jason in *Bad Teacher*
27 "You're looking at him!"
28 ___ *Like It Hot* (1959)
29 Homophone of air
30 Baseball Hall of Fame sights
31 *CHiPS* star Estrada
32 *Ben-Hur* setting
33 *The Daily Beast* founder
36 Lexis-Nexis offering
37 Like ski resorts
39 Rockefeller Center muralist
40 Concert pit
42 Voice box
43 Southern DR Congo city
45 East China Sea island
46 *Mr. Palomar* author Calvino
47 Machine handle
48 *The First Wives Club* wife
49 Some bowlers
50 German for "genuine"
51 "Hey, sailor!"
52 CNBC anchor Burnett

A Cup of Joe

Do you know your (black) stuff?
See if you're wide awake enough to pick the right answers about coffee.

1. *Espresso* literally means:
   a. Speed it up
   b. To go
   c. Forced out
   d. Black and intense

2. Forty percent of the world's coffee is produced by:
   a. Africa
   b. Colombia and Brazil
   c. Turkey
   d. Southeast Asia

3. An *ibrik* is:
   a. A South American tool for grinding coffee beans
   b. The Turkish word for *barista*
   c. A Middle Eastern coffeehouse
   d. A long-handled copper pot for making Turkish coffee

4. Kopi Luwak, the world's most expensive coffee (up to $600 per pound), is:
   a. Processed during a full moon
   b. Brewed only with solid gold pots
   c. Made from coffee beans eaten and excreted by a Sumatran wildcat
   d. Grown at a higher altitude than any other bean

5. Arabica varieties such as Java and Mocha are named after:
   a. The plantations where they're grown
   b. The coffee grower who developed that variety
   c. Their predominant flavorings
   d. Their ports of origin

6. The name *cappuccino* comes from:
   a. The drink's resemblance to the brown cowls worn by Capuchin monks
   b. The similarity in color to the fur of Capuchin monkeys
   c. The Italian *puccino*, meaning "light brown one"
   d. The size of the cup in which it's commonly served

7. Most coffees are a blend of:
   a. Light and dark roasts
   b. Caffeine and essential oils
   c. Arabica and robusta beans
   d. African and South American beans

8. Coffee beans grow on:
   a. A low, spreading vine
   b. A bush
   c. A tree
   d. The roots of a coffee plant

9. Coffee was the first food to be:
   a. Shipped from Europe to the New World
   b. Freeze-dried
   c. Used in Aztec religious ceremonies
   d. Roasted and ground for drinking

10. Sixteenth-century Muslim rulers banned coffee because of:
    a. Its stimulating effects
    b. The gambling that took place in coffeehouses
    c. The black market that sprang up in the coffee trade
    d. Sufi mystics who wanted coffee limited to spiritual ceremonies

BRAINSNACK® # Canvas

What color (1-4) should the white area on the canvas be painted?

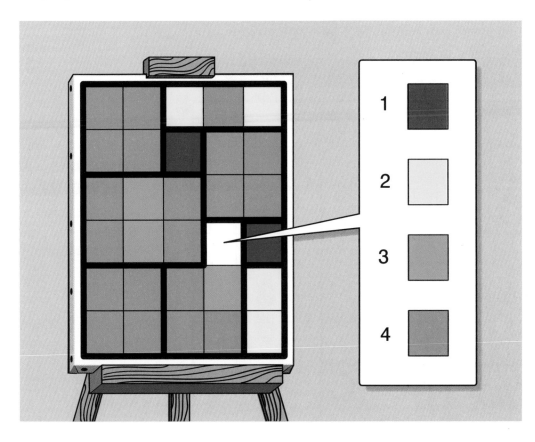

Put a letter in each of the squares below to make a word that means "journey."

These numbered clues refer to other words that can be made from the whole:

2 7 1 10 5 2 3 ENDANGER; 4 8 5 4 3 10 LIQUID CLEANSE;
5 10 4 8 3 ROYAL; 4 8 3 10 WIND.

1	2	3	4	5	6	7	8	9	10

Word Sudoku

Complete the grid so that each row, each column and each 3 x 3 frame contains the nine letters from the black box below. The hidden nine-letter word is in the diagonal from top left to bottom right.

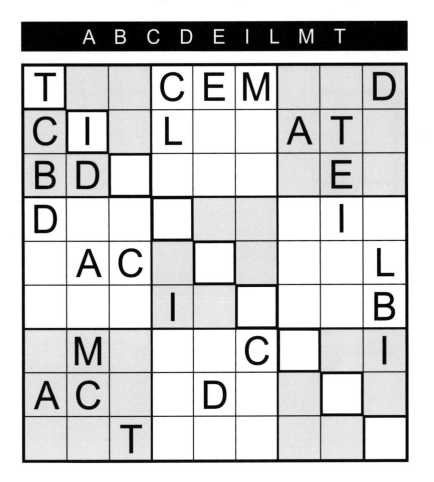

A B C D E I L M T

T			C	E	M			D
C	I		L			A	T	
B	D						E	
D							I	
	A	C						L
			I					B
	M				C			I
A	C			D				
		T						

do you KNOW?

Which chemical element has the shortest name?

_____

_____

TRANSADDITION

Add two letters to **UNSENT WIRE** and rearrange the rest to find a connection.

_____

122

Sport Maze

Draw the shortest way from the ball to the goal. You can only move along vertical and horizontal lines, not along diagonal lines. The figure on each square indicates the number of squares the ball must be moved in the same direction. You can change direction at each stop.

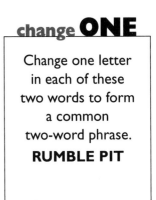

change ONE

Change one letter in each of these two words to form a common two-word phrase.
RUMBLE PIT

ONE LETTER LESS OR MORE

The word on the right side contains the letters of the word on the left side plus or minus the letter in the middle. One letter is already in the right place.

B A C H E L O R -B [ ] [ ] [ ] L [ ] [ ] [ ]

National Dairy Month

ACROSS

1 "The ___ bitsy spider..."
5 And others (abbrev.)
9 Representative (abbrev.)
12 ___ man (debt collector)
13 Soda
14 Owed
15 Catch, as on a sweater
16 Milk-producing cow
18 Once ___ a time
20 Formal hairstyle
21 ___ Dame
24 Dairy product
26 Join together
27 Family
28 Name before Iver and Jovi (musical groups)
29 TV singing competition *The ___*
31 Spring month
34 Finale
35 Hanging open
37 Dairy product
41 Divisions
42 Steals from
43 Christmas song
45 Dairy treat (2 words)
48 Land measure
52 Big ___, CA
53 ___ mater
54 Places for a bath
55 West Coast time (abbrev.)
56 Appearance, aspect
57 Dog in *Garfield* comic

DOWN

1 Uncle Sam's tax collector (abbrev.)
2 Perfect score
3 Pampering place
4 Dairy product
5 Canyon sound
6 Animated show, for short
7 Everything
8 ___ Vegas
9 Skillful
10 Hike leader
11 Male choir member
17 Egyptian king
19 Annoys
21 Small piece
22 Yoko ___
23 Old roofing material
24 Pen brand name
25 Discomfort
27 Child
30 Loneliest number
31 Buddy
32 Likely
33 Word of agreement
36 Dairy product popular in Italy
37 Crunchy
38 ___-pocus
39 Film critic Roger
40 Keyboard key (abbrev.)
43 Title
44 Country next to Yemen
46 Male sheep
47 Actor Wallach
49 A cow chews it
50 Baseball stat (abbrev.)
51 Compass direction opposite WNW

Sudoku X

Fill in the grid so that each row, each column and each 3 x 3 frame contains every number from 1 to 9. The two main diagonals of the grid also contain every number from 1 to 9.

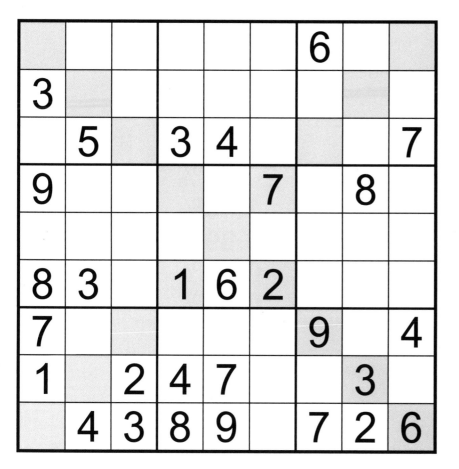

SANDWICH

What five-letter word belongs between the word at left and the word at right, so that the first and second word, and the second and third word, each form a common compound word or phrase?

HORSE _ _ _ _ _ HOUSE

BRAINSNACK® Seedless

100% pure Burgundian grape juice, made from grape pulp, consists of the following percentages of water, sugars, tannin, acids, cellulose and minerals in order from top to bottom. Which percentage is wrong?

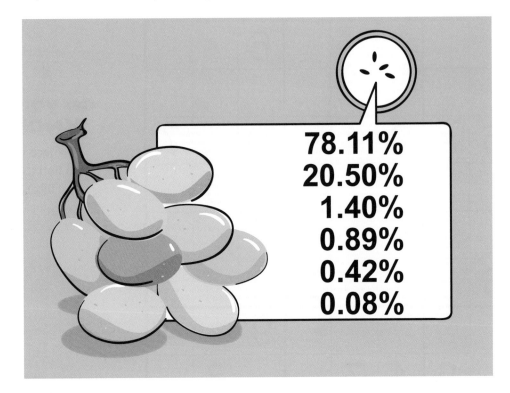

78.11%
20.50%
1.40%
0.89%
0.42%
0.08%

END GAME

The words you are seeking all have the letters END in them in the position indicated.
When you have found all of the answers, with help from the clues on the right, one column will reveal the END GAME word and give you a shade.

__	__	__	E	N	D	__	__	Meant
__	__	__	E	N	D	__	__	Sociable
__	E	N	D	__	__	__	__	Flexible
__	__	__	E	N	D__	__	__	Abandoned

CROSSWORD # Johnny Mercer Songs

ACROSS

1 Red and Black, for two
5 Johnny Mercer's "Days of Wine and ___"
10 Concert equipment
14 Paquin in *The Piano*
15 "101" class, briefly
16 Foot part
17 Mercer song sung by Diana Krall
19 Acerbic
20 Blackouts
21 Peculiar
23 Tom Clancy fan
24 "Abie Baby" musical
25 "I Loves You, Porgy" singer
27 Answered
30 Alpha followers
33 Briny drops
35 "West Point of the South"
36 ___-TASS
37 "Dream Lover" singer
38 "I'll ___ touch"
39 Big Mac part
40 Actress Gray and others
41 Specialty
42 Like Archie Bunker
44 Russia-China border river
46 *American Beauty* novelist Ferber
47 "Oops!" list
51 Wes Craven horror films
54 Furrowed
55 Goddess of strife
56 Mercer song sung by Frank Sinatra
58 Wine casks
59 *Paradise Lost* angel
60 "___ Quam Videri" (NC motto)
61 Thought
62 Large flower
63 Go-getter

DOWN

1 Taste
2 Happen next
3 Vampire hunter Blake
4 Restaurant buffet option
5 "Memphis" singer Johnny
6 Singles
7 Hog heaven
8 Son of Ares
9 Baptist type
10 Assault
11 Mercer song sung by Andy Williams
12 Stopper
13 All dried out
18 Gothic arches
22 Talks in rhyme
26 A bit starchy
27 Mrs. Gorbachev
28 Beam
29 Break bread
30 Light green lettuce
31 Manicurist's case
32 Mercer song recorded by Jimmy Dorsey
34 Maritime eagle
37 Concocts
38 On loan
40 Volcano near Messina
41 Angry display
43 Yakov Smirnoff's birthplace
45 No more than
48 Dispatch boat
49 Keyed-up
50 Math machine
51 ET-seeking org.
52 Sludge
53 "Absolutely!"
54 *The X-Files* extras
57 "O Sole ___"

No one, including Walt Disney himself, expected *Snow White and the Seven Dwarfs* to do well when the film premiered in late 1937. It was nicknamed Disney's Folly and cost about $1.5 million—unheard of for the time. Of course, audiences loved it and still do.

HOW MUCH DO YOU RECALL OF THIS ANIMATED GEM?

1 What are the names of the seven dwarfs?

_____

2 Where are the dwarfs coming from when they sing, "Heigh-ho, heigh-ho, it's home from work we go"?

_____

3 Who is the only dwarf who doesn't speak?

_____

4 **True or False?** *Snow White* was nominated for an Oscar for outstanding production (best picture).

_____

5 **True or False?** *Snow White* was the first film to have a separately released movie soundtrack.

_____

6 Not counting video, DVD or Blu-ray releases or film-festival showings, *Snow White* has been rereleased in movie theaters how many times since the 1930s?

A) 10   B) 15   C) 8   D) 22

_____

TEST YOUR RECALL

What popular roadster introduced in 1932 could achieve speed of over 135 miles per hour?

_____

Cage the Animals

Draw lines to completely divide up the grid into small squares with exactly one animal per square. The squares should not overlap.

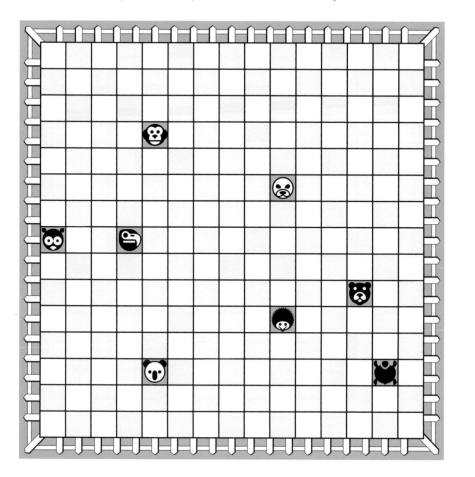

do you KNOW?

What is the analysis of pebbles called?

_____

_____

LETTERBLOCKS

Move the letterblocks around so that words are formed on top and below that are associated with athletics

D L H E R S U
E L J I V N A

State-of-the-Art

ACROSS

1 Rip Van Winkle's dog
5 Couldn't hide one's astonishment
10 Use a whetstone
14 Bittersweet coating
15 Where Socrates shopped
16 Jim Davis dog
17 San ___ (Riviera resort)
18 Hawaii's "Pineapple Island"
19 Croissant
20 NEW YORK and KENTUCKY
23 "Echoes" singer Williams
24 2008 Rose Bowl winners
25 Calls it a career
29 Affliction
33 "Lest we lose our ___": Browning
34 Partner of wash
36 Quagmire
37 TENNESSEE
41 *Avatar* extras
42 Ford crossover
43 A lot of cattle
44 1992 John Goodman film
47 Zonked
49 Beavers of the Pac-12
50 18-wheeler
51 MAINE
60 "Away in a Manger," for one
61 Roman fountain
62 *Haliaeetus albicilla*
63 Run in neutral
64 "Bat Out of Hell" singer Foley
65 Number worn by Roger Maris
66 *Beverly Hills Cop* org.
67 *A Study in Scarlet* author
68 A shade of blue

DOWN

1 "Close"
2 "Milk's favorite cookie"
3 Delineate
4 Result of a gully washer
5 Abounding
6 "Got ___ named Daisy ..."
7 Shelty
8 La Belle Epoch et al.
9 Frozen cocktail
10 *Ars Poetica* poet
11 Musk, for one
12 Cleo barged down it
13 "Beautiful Freak" group
21 Analyze grammatically
22 *Arizona* letters
25 Put at 000
26 Meathead's mother-in-law
27 Under stress
28 Jesper Parnevik, for one
29 Claire in *Little Women*
30 "Come, Watson, the game's ___ !"
31 Start a match
32 Finalized
35 Tiny fraction of a joule
38 Answered a debater
39 Ace Rickenbacker
40 Bit
45 Cooked crawfish
46 Cerastes
48 White weasel
51 Deep blue
52 Belly-wash
53 Beatles film
54 Architect's plinth
55 Put trust in
56 Robbie Knievel's dad
57 French cheese
58 Birthplace of Ceres
59 Lurch

Sudoku

Fill in the grid so that each row, each column and each 3 x 3 frame contains every number from 1 to 9.

					7			
						3		
		3					8	1
				9				
8						4	9	6
4	9	7		6		1		
7	4	2	5	8	6			
6		5	3					7
3		9	4					8

do you KNOW

Which composer wrote *Water Music*?

_____

_____

FRIENDS

What do the following words have in common?

ANGEL BISHOP DEACON DUCHESS DUKE ENEMY WAY

_____

Sunny

Where will the sun shine, if each arrow points in the direction of a spot where the symbol is located? The symbols cannot be next to each other vertically, horizontally or diagonally. A symbol cannot be placed on top of an arrow. We show one symbol.

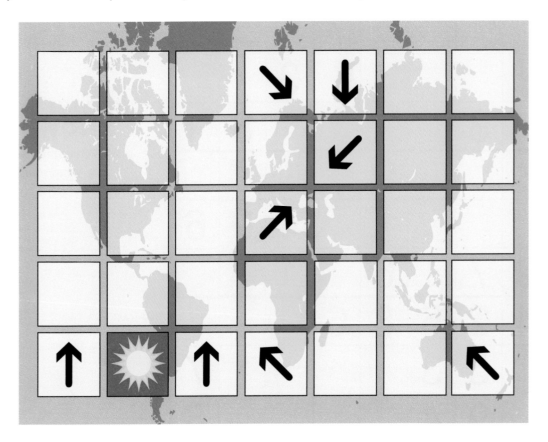

BLOCK ANAGRAM

Form the words that are described in the brackets with the letters above the grid. Extra letters are already in the right place.

MERCILESS (bomb)

CROSSWORD   Mellow Yellow

ACROSS

1 Duck dog
4 Delany of *Pasadena*
8 Jewish grandma
13 Prefix for biology
14 Mosconi shot
15 Baseball great Buck
16 Yellow Manhattan vehicles
19 Microsoft cofounder Paul
20 Factotum
21 Job at a gas station
22 Communicate manually
24 Estimator's phrase
26 Yellow condiment
32 Mercury or Saturn
33 Oise water
34 Steinbeck migrants
36 Letters after Sen. Shaheen's name
37 Camera accessory
40 Average grade
41 Decalogue mount
43 1969 Peace Nobelist: Abbrev.
44 Gumbo pod
45 Yellow birds
49 Of flying craft
50 Let off steam
51 Nas hit
54 Prefix for dextrous
56 W African country
60 Floral yellow
63 Overthrow, e.g.
64 Nick in *The Good Thief* star
65 Thurman in *Final Analysis*
66 Curling, e.g.
67 Aid a felon
68 Tattoo word

DOWN

1 Olin in *The Reader*
2 Boitano jump
3 Hollowware item
4 ___ es Salaam
5 Little Rock resident
6 Reply to the Little Red Hen
7 Spongy tinder
8 "Sk8er ___": Avril Lavigne
9 Take the wraps off
10 Boyfriend
11 Light green lettuce
12 Besides
14 Like a dunce cap
17 Kind of question
18 Gen-___ (boomers' kids)
23 Indian butter
25 "Whoa!"
26 They come and go
27 Like Viking letters
28 Prefix for centric
29 Ragtime, e.g.
30 *Gigli* heroine
31 "John ___ Tractor": Judds
35 Third Day creation
37 Fruit of the Keys
38 Collarbone
39 Top-notch
42 ___ *All Seasons* (1966)
44 Prefix for pedic
46 Toward the mouth
47 Latin names
48 Go after trout
51 Caesar's bad day
52 Nag
53 Beehive's kin
55 Spout like a whale
57 Calla lily
58 Disney clownfish
59 Aussie golfer Scott
61 Kitchen scrap
62 "Master Melvin" of baseball

Number Cluster

Cubes showing numbers have been placed on the grid below with some spaces left empty. Can you complete the grid by creating runs of the same number and of the same length as the number? So where a cube with number 5 has been included on the grid you need to create a run of five number 5's, including the cube already shown. The run can be horizontal, vertical or both horizontal and vertical.

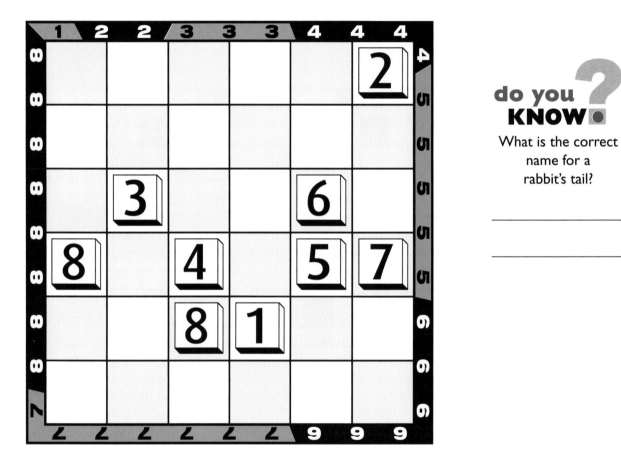

MISSING LETTER PROVERB

Fill in each missing letter, indicated by an X, to make a well-known proverb.

XEEX XXXX XOWXEX XRX

BRAIN FITNESS Letter Search #2

In the grid below, find all appearances of the letter N, both capital and lowercase, any color. When you are ready, set a stopwatch or note the time. Circle every letter N. Then go back and count how many appear in capital and how many in lowercase. Finally, count how many Ns appear in blue. Note how long it took you, and see if you can beat your time in the other letter searches.

FOR THIS EXERCISE, YOU'LL NEED:
A pen or pencil • A stopwatch or watch or clock with a second hand

K	a	N	M	r	r	N	c	N	m	n	k	A	r	X	c	X	m	x	r	N	a
k	R	n	n	r	k	r	X	B	k	k	M	z	N	r	n	k	r	X	N	Z	N
a	x	m	Z	r	R	r	K	Z	N	X	k	R	X	n	k	k	n	R	a	k	X
x	r	x	n	Z	k	m	X	R	r	Z	c	m	x	Z	r	Z	m	X	Z	r	R
m	Z	c	Z	N	a	Z	n	Z	R	m	N	r	R	M	z	A	Z	m	c	k	R
R	m	z	n	X	r	Z	m	N	K	z	x	N	a	z	R	z	M	r	z	X	r
X	z	N	k	m	M	c	z	Z	r	c	X	R	N	n	z	K	R	a	K	k	n
c	m	z	R	z	k	c	M	N	Z	x	m	z	B	a	x	X	M	R	X	m	m
x	X	N	z	m	r	R	x	A	X	n	z	m	Z	X	N	z	M	n	X	a	X
n	X	A	k	r	n	m	x	R	a	X	R	R	r	m	c	R	n	B	a	k	z
k	x	z	M	Z	k	N	z	m	R	N	X	a	k	r	R	x	r	k	X	r	X
B	Z	r	X	r	K	a	Z	B	z	R	z	N	A	k	M	x	X	c	R	n	A
r	X	n	x	a	R	M	k	k	Z	x	r	X	k	a	c	K	x	R	n	R	z
c	x	z	N	R	x	c	M	m	R	n	z	B	M	x	R	z	n	R	z	x	M
N	R	r	R	z	r	R	n	Z	R	n	m	R	A	a	X	X	r	m	R	n	Z
R	z	R	z	N	z	B	x	R	R	r	Z	x	R	n	X	a	z	m	R	x	n
c	x	z	N	R	x	c	M	m	R	n	z	B	M	x	R	z	n	R	z	x	M
n	x	z	M	Z	k	N	z	m	R	N	X	a	k	r	R	x	r	k	X	r	X
R	m	z	n	X	r	Z	m	N	K	z	x	N	a	z	R	z	M	r	z	X	r

TIME _____   NUMBER OF CAPITAL Ns_____

NUMBER OF LOWERCASE Ns_____   NUMBER OF BLUE Ns_____

CROSSWORD Frosty Airs

ACROSS

1 Short mornings
4 British isle
9 Sign
14 Romantic narrative poem
15 Dike, Eunomia, and Irene
16 Suffix with moth
17 St. Pierre is one
18 "Here We Come ___"
20 Aussie girls
22 Unlucky fisherman's catch
23 Source of gallic acid
24 Hangman's rope
25 Airbus product
28 32K ounces
29 Narcissus relatives
31 Clavell's *Tai-___*
33 Freshman 15, for one
35 Tone deafness
36 Covent Garden song
38 Crane or heron
40 Frankenstein's gofer
41 MBA or MSA
43 Poet Juana ___ de la Cruz
45 Army COs
46 Under little pressure, say
48 Agony
50 Memo abbrev.
51 Dated term for a college girl
52 Sweeney Todd, for one
55 Wild cat
56 Undeceptive
57 Sharps and flats
61 Trevino or Elder
62 Platter player
63 Argentine dance
64 Laptop display
65 Lone Star State
66 Merlin in *Little House on the Prairie*
67 Easy and Wall

DOWN

1 Tilting, asea
2 Sharapova's nickname
3 A Christmas carol
4 Activity loathed by Greenpeace
5 Des Moines denizen
6 Fat, in New Orleans
7 Owns
8 Stand the ___ time
9 Eccentrics
10 Breathing sound
11 "Like ___ love it!"
12 "Good" casino card
13 Essex loc.
19 United charge
21 Daughter of Harmonia
24 Encrusted with sugar
25 A Christmas carol
26 J. Alfred Prufrock's creator
27 Some Fabergé egg owners
29 24 horas
30 "Where ___ Begin?"
31 *The Taming of the Shrew* setting
32 Question opener
34 "Groovy!"
37 Macaw genus
39 Result
42 Cape Verde coins
44 Kristy in *The Phantom*
47 Makeshift shelter
49 Frodo's foe
52 Part of a hull
53 Construct
54 Clarinet and oboe
55 Choreographer Bausch
56 Lacking
57 Given
58 4th Spanish letter
59 Courteney of *Friends*
60 Guitarist Farlow

Binairo

Complete the grid with zeros and ones until there are 5 zeros and 6 ones in every row and every column. No more than two of the same number can be next to or under each other. Rows or columns with exactly the same content are not allowed. There is only one valid solution.

do you KNOW?

What is L. Frank Baum's most famous story?

_____

_____

REPOSITION PREPOSITION

Unscramble **HAT KNOTS** and find a two-word preposition.

_____

Spot the Differences

Find the nine differences in the image on the bottom right.

do you KNOW?

What note does an
orchestra tune to?

_____

_____

trivia

● What was the name of the project,
headed by J. Robert Oppenheimer,
to create the first atomic bomb?

_____

CROSSWORD Summer Picnic

ACROSS
1 Two electricity types (abbrev.)
5 Win
9 Singer Marley or Dylan
12 Ark builder
13 Too
14 Building wing
15 China desert
16 Drink for a picnic
18 ___ Mix (cereal snack)
20 Bargains
21 Slows down
24 Ask forgiveness
25 Mature
26 "The Eagle ___ landed"
27 Sign
28 Dance
29 ___ in the belfry
33 A white fish
34 Poet TS
35 Easter animal
39 Music award
40 Once more
41 Chinese money
42 Popular picnic cuisine
44 Popular veggie for chips
48 Wall Street abbreviation
49 The red planet
50 Paradise
51 Family room
52 Unwelcome picnic guests
53 Croaker

DOWN
1 Director Lee
2 Pigeon sound
3 Dollop
4 Fried ___, picnic favorite
5 Weather that ruins a picnic
6 Game show host Trebek
7 Suffix meaning "belief"
8 Hangman's loops
9 Street in Memphis
10 Ancient
11 Archaic form of "hallowed"
17 Snooze
19 Egg layer
21 Sib of sis
22 Edge
23 Primate
24 Old towel
26 Concealed
28 ___ down (take notes)
29 Where to spread out a picnic
30 Goal
31 Actor Hanks or Cruise
32 Pig pen
33 Movie theater
34 Time period
35 Fanatical
36 Selfless love
37 Low-ranking nobleman
38 Baby's garment
39 Take a stab at
41 Circular tent
43 Open a ___ of worms
45 Much ___ About Nothing
46 Field
47 Finish

Keep Going

Start on a blank square of your choice and connect as many blank squares as possible with one single continuous line. You can only connect squares along vertical and horizontal lines, not along diagonal lines. You must continue the connecting line up until the next obstacle, i.e., the rim of the box, a black square or a square that has already been used. You can change direction at any obstacle you meet. Each square can only be used once. The number of blank squares that will be left unused is marked in the upper square. There is more than one solution. We only show one solution.

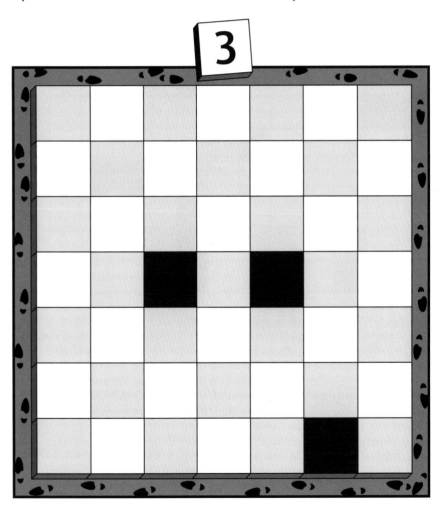

delete **ONE**

Delete one letter from
ORATORS HATE
and rearrange the rest to find a speaker's fear.

WORD SEARCH # Exercise

All the words are hidden vertically, horizontally or diagonally—in both directions. The letters that remain unused form a sentence from left to right.

```
E E D E M O N S T R A T E X P
E V S H O W E R R W C I S U A
M R O F R E P E O K E E Y P C
S Y B M E T A R E P O D D L E
B O S R U F K I T M I R D E T
A M W N E V I S I T A B A A O
W D I K E A E P A P S R N V A
A N M L Y O K U E U R E C E N
L E B H C O D A N Y N A E H D
K D R W S B E L W S S T I G F
H R T O A A O B T A W H E I R
T A H T B A W A U I Y E O R O
P G H N D I C H E I A E L P E
A E C O O K C F O L L O W T S
I N S T A L L H Y C L D I M C
N F I G H T E I Y S C R U B A
T R A V E L A C G N I S T S P
L L O R T S N S S E N T I F E
```

- AEROBIC
- BATHE
- BREAK AWAY
- BREATHE
- BUILD
- CLEAN
- CLIMB
- COOK
- CYCLE
- DANCE
- DEMONSTRATE
- DRAPE
- ESCAPE
- FIGHT
- FITNESS
- FOLLOW
- GARDEN
- INSTALL
- LEAVE
- MARCH
- MOVE
- OPERATE
- PACE TO AND FRO
- PAINT
- PERFORM
- SAUNTER
- SCRUB
- SHOP
- SHOWER
- SING
- STACK
- STROLL
- SWIM
- TIDY UP
- TRAVEL
- UNLOAD
- VISIT
- WALK
- WASH
- WORK

CROSSWORD **How Sweet!**

ACROSS

1 "Hallelujah" singer k.d.
5 Mortify
10 RAM units, for short
14 "Et ___" (and others)
15 Forearm bones
16 A voided escutcheon
17 *Gilligan's Island* tree
18 Baby beds
19 Plaintiff
20 Sweet presentation graph?
22 Tiny perfume bottle
24 Futhark character
25 Adds turf to
26 Breadcrumb paste
29 Screeched
33 Sporty Camaro
34 Anticipate
35 *7 Faces of Dr. ___* (1964)
36 Sweet former Buffalo Bills fullback?
40 CIA forerunner
41 *Jurassic Park* dinosaur, e.g.
42 Feed the kitty
43 Cutting canines
45 Adjourn briefly
47 Promising
48 "Catch a ___": Beach Boys
49 *The Namesake* author
52 Sweet Ragtime dance?
56 "Wild blue yonder" org.
57 A Middle Easterner
59 Cumming in *Burlesque*
60 *Finding Nemo* fish
61 Very good ratings
62 Pair of oxen
63 "___ on Down the Road"
64 Hide away
65 Ratatouille

DOWN

1 Arctic Circle inhabitant
2 Russian range
3 *Aida* backdrop
4 Trifle
5 Deep secrets
6 Ballet rail
7 Access for a collier
8 Mary-Kate, to Ashley
9 Like Don Larsen's perfect game
10 Salon foam
11 At one time, once
12 Jane Lynch series
13 Visionary
21 1963 Martin Ritt film
23 *All in the Family* character
25 Source of oil
26 Embroidery loop
27 "Mighty Lak' ___"
28 *Hang 'Em High* prop
29 Benny Goodman's era
30 *A Fish Called Wanda* Oscar winner
31 90° headings
32 Fusses over
34 Heartache
37 Blood of the gods
38 Letter drop-offs
39 Stockcar venues
44 Trinket
45 Licentious
46 Simpson of *Murder, She Wrote*
48 Abates
49 Winter Olympics event
50 Argento in *Marie Antoinette*
51 "Archers of St. George" artist
52 Miracle site in John 2:1
53 Oodles
54 Titicaca or Tahoe
55 "If You ___ Susie"
58 Buzz Aldrin's alma mater

142

Word Sudoku

Complete the grid so that each row, each column and each 3 x 3 frame contains the nine letters from the black box below. The hidden nine-letter word is in the diagonal from top left to bottom right.

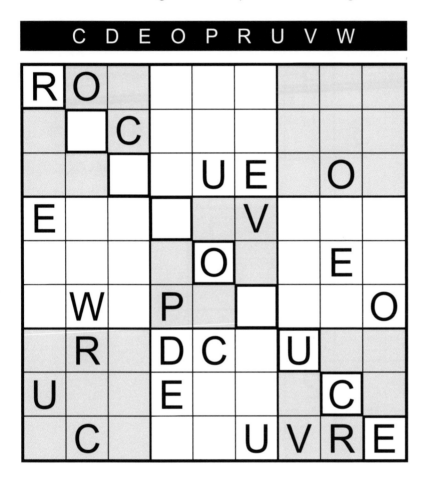

C D E O P R U V W

do you KNOW?

What animal is the source of cashmere?

_____

_____

UNCANNY TURN

Rearrange the letters of the phrase to form a cognate anagram, one which is related or connected in meaning to the original phrase. The answer can be one or more words.

ABLY SEDUCED US

Sudoku

Fill in the grid so that each row, each column and each 3 x 3 frame contains every number from 1 to 9.

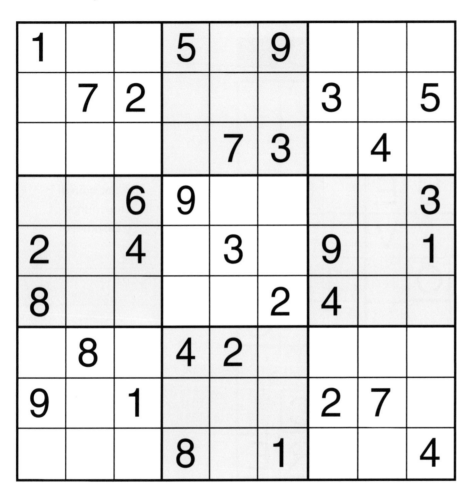

triVia • What do these have in common: McKinley, Aconagua, Kilimanjaro, Kosciusko?

_____

MIND MAZE Pairing Up

Test your ability to match these multi-colored puzzles, like with like.

FIT THE PIECES
How might these six shapes be paired to form three perfect squares?

LOCK TOGETHER
Can you find the three perfect circles that can be made by matching these spindly shapes?

Sport Maze

Draw the shortest way from the ball to the goal. You can only move along vertical and horizontal lines, not along diagonal lines. The figure on each square indicates the number of squares the ball must be moved in the same direction. You can change direction at each stop.

2	1	4	4	2	3
2	3	3	2	2	1
1	2	1	2	2	2
5	4	3	3	4	5
2	4	4	2	1	5
	1	1	4	1	3

change ONE

Change one letter in each of these two words to form a common two-word phrase.

SHOOTING
CATCH

ONE LETTER LESS OR MORE

The word on the right side contains the letters of the word on the left side plus or minus the letter in the middle. One letter is already in the right place.

MAGAZINE -E ☐ ☐ ☐ Z ☐ ☐ ☐

146

CROSSWORD Themeless

ACROSS
1 61 subject
6 Minor to-do
10 Talk trash
14 Like Crusoe before Friday
15 RPM instrument
16 Cut glass
17 Blooming early
18 Meddle
20 A, B, and C
22 Became itinerant
23 Cream of the crop
24 Picture puzzles
25 "Cowboy's Lament" city
27 Steen's stand
28 Tony Romo targets
29 Aida's native land
31 Shell food?
35 *Bleak House* girl
36 16-oz. units
37 *Dracula* director Browning
38 "Amazing Grace," e.g.
40 Struck a low blow
42 Golfer Irwin
43 Tale of Troy
45 Adds a rider to
47 Bawdy
50 "Dear" book
51 *Guys and Dolls* gambler Detroit
52 Like chronicles of the past
55 False
57 Beehive-shaped crown
58 Bittersweet coating
59 ___ plaisir!
60 Step onstage
61 Bucolic expanses
62 Acuff and Clark
63 About one-ninth of an orchestra

DOWN
1 "Terrif!"
2 Kirghizian range
3 Netherlands city
4 Inspires
5 Apparently was
6 Service hitch
7 *Iron Chef* props
8 Play God?
9 *Black Widow* actress Russell
10 A fate worse than debt
11 Romantic pairs
12 Hillside debris
13 Backyard buildings
19 Housecoat
21 Religious painting
24 Striker's demand
25 "Ah!___!" (Donnie Iris song)
26 Murray of tennis
27 Abated
30 Arm bones
32 "Be that as it may ..."
33 Like vichyssoise
34 Pablo Neruda poems
39 *The Graduate* director
40 *As Good As It Gets* actor Greg
41 Place for a speaker
42 Anne of Green Gables, e.g.
44 Low-fat
46 Substance
47 Shaq of basketball
48 Fonteyn's rail
49 Anatomical furrow
50 Harrow blades
52 "Hip to Be Square" rocker Lewis
53 All het up
54 "Drive" band
56 Ab ___ (from the beginning)

CROSSWORD **Best Picture**

ACROSS

1 Foot problem
5 Event at a cross-country meet
9 Type of dive
13 Boring (slang)
14 All of the ___
16 Author Hoag
17 Elsa's sister in *Frozen*
18 *The Dirty* ___
19 Prince William's former school
20 Best Picture of 1964 *My* ___ (2 wds.)
22 Horse rider Paul
24 Metallic rock
25 Politician Ralph
26 Fancy ties
30 Theater section
31 Retainer
34 Bounds
35 Capital of Normandy
36 Toyota ___4
37 Loser's place
38 Best Picture of 1965 *The* ___ *of Music*
39 Activist Parks
40 7th letter of the Greek alphabet
41 Stockpile
42 Went from full phase to new
43 Name for some hills
44 Word before weight or count
45 Child's toy
46 Root veggies
48 Heroic Spanish leader El ___
49 Pure
51 Best Picture of 1939 ___ *the Wind* (2 wds.)
56 Litter's tiny tot
57 Chestnut horses
59 4,840 square yards
60 Formerly

61 Catty
62 Act
63 School groups
64 "Country" Slaughter
65 Chick noise

DOWN

1 Snowman friend of 17 Across
2 1940s star Andrews
3 Hotel chain
4 Word before admiral
5 Meteorologists use them
6 House
7 Snug
8 Best Picture of 1950 *All About* ___
9 McQueen of *Bullitt*

10 Best Picture of 1954 *On the* ___
11 Love in Spain
12 Number of lives for Fluffy
15 Furious
21 Housing parcels
23 The first garden
25 People, places and things
26 Shoe company ___ Edmonds
27 "From ___ shining sea" (2 wds.)
28 Best Picture of 1943
29 Choose
30 Rotten
32 Painter's stand
33 Avoid

35 Highways
38 Barbecue devices
39 Fink
41 Help in misdeeds
42 Act like a shorebird
45 Preps dishes for the dishwasher
47 ___ Park, Colorado
48 Real estate unit
49 Corn or soy beans, perhaps
50 Search
51 Profit
52 Buzzy stinger
53 Slurpee competitor
54 Willow, for example
55 Cannabis plant
58 Best Picture of 1934 *It Happened* ___ *Night*

Cage the Animals

Draw lines to completely divide up the grid into small squares with exactly one animal per square. The squares should not overlap.

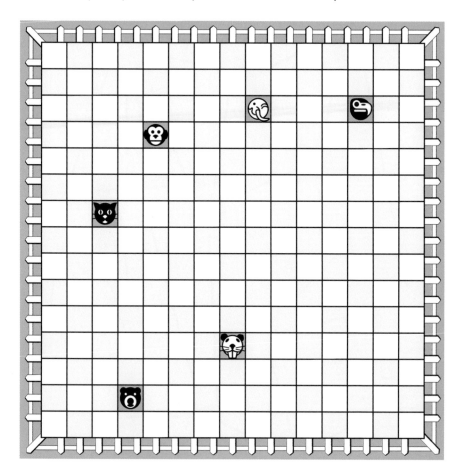

do you KNOW?

Which superhero has a butler named Alfred?

_____

_____

LETTERBLOCKS

Move the letterblocks around so that words are formed on top and below that you would associate with cars.

L C L N I O N
R C M R E U Y

Constellation

Follow the black lines from S to F. To make it more difficult, you may only move from one shape to the next if they have the same shape and/or color.

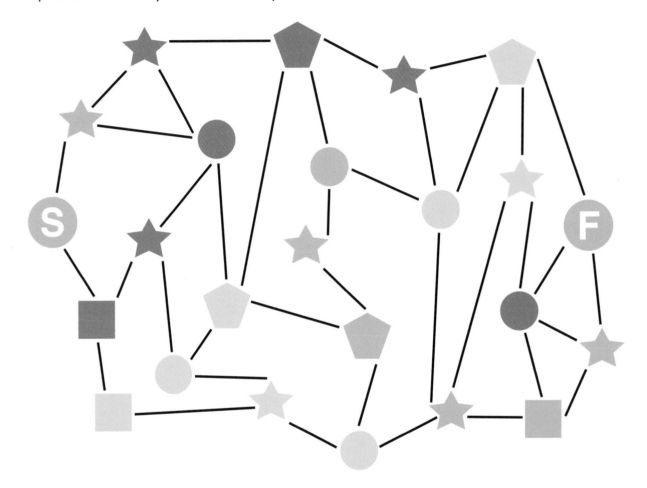

triVia • One of the characters in Shakespeare's play *A Midsummer Night's Dream* is the victim of a spell that puts a donkey's head on his shoulders.

What is his name?

CROSSWORD TV Westerns

ACROSS

1 Cereal or board game
5 Hairless
9 Like a city street
14 Dry
15 Code with three numbers
16 Type of oil
17 *The* _____, TV Western set on Shiloh Ranch
19 Jason's mythical wife
20 Attribute
21 Judge
23 Grade school class
24 Confederates (abbrev.)
27 Under the radar
29 TV Western with Marshal Matt Dillon
33 Everything
34 Had dinner
35 *Nina* and *Santa Maria*
37 City in Iowa
41 Shakespeare
43 Repair a football field
45 Dress in India
46 Mary Jane, for example
47 Cobbled
49 _____ rummy
50 Golfer Trevino
53 TV Western starring James Garner
55 Enlarged
59 Character
60 Doctor's org.
61 Treble, for one
63 Discernment
67 Actress Greta
69 *The* _____, TV Western with matriarch Victoria Barkley (2 words)
72 Flirt
73 Glimmer
74 Ditty
75 Author Zora _____ Hurston
76 Honk
77 Hankerings

DOWN

1 Hawaiian rock
2 Spring bloom
3 Balsam and Douglas
4 Lawn tools
5 Outlaw
6 Onassis nickname
7 Atomic number 82
8 Copenhagen residents
9 Stationary horse
10 Ginger _____
11 Hairstylist Sassoon
12 Tennis great Chris
13 _____ *Valley Days*, TV Western
18 Bullet points
22 Airport abbreviation
25 Physicist Niels
26 "Blue _____, smiling at me"
28 Regrettably
29 Chats
30 Home of Arches National Park
31 Famous fiddler?
32 Healing salt
36 Word before panel or system
38 Wise men
39 Guitarist Clapton
40 Kitchen _____
42 Remove
44 "Whip It" band
48 Faucet brand
51 Concert finale
52 Sometime sushi ingredient
54 Company such as Century 21
55 _____ *Train*, TV Western
56 Mirror product
57 *Finding Nemo* villain
58 Type of card
62 Name for a dog
64 Turn
65 Volunteer State (abbrev.)
66 Peepers
68 _____ Canto
70 Before synchronous and stationary
71 Tub

Languages

All the words are hidden vertically, horizontally or diagonally—in both directions. The letters that remain unused form a sentence from left to right.

```
A L B A N I A N E S P E C R A
D A N I S H N G T O I S I A N
A R T T I F I R C I A L B L W
S A A N G U A E G E T H A E A
L G D T W A S E H C N E R F C
O R E U E A T K H E D B A C E
V P O R T U G U E S E S A S O
E T H U M C A T D H I T E I F
N F E S R A H E S P A N I S H
I N T S C C N U L L I T N U R
A H S I K R U T A H T E A I S
N I L A M O S N C K A C I O F
U B E N G A L I L A L D S U H
N T I B E T A N D Z I E R C R
S N A A K I R F A A A S E Z T
A N D E N A E R O K N Z P U A
H S I L G N E C H O C T H L E
H S I L O P S E R B I A N U R
```

- AFRIKAANS
- ALBANIAN
- ARABIC
- BENGALI
- CATALAN
- CHINESE
- CROATIAN
- CZECH
- DANISH
- DUTCH
- ENGLISH
- FINNISH
- FRENCH
- GERMAN
- GREEK
- HEBREW
- ITALIAN
- KAZAKH
- KOREAN
- LATIN
- PERSIAN
- POLISH
- PORTUGUESE
- RUSSIAN
- SERBIAN
- SLOVENIAN
- SOMALI
- SPANISH
- TIBETAN
- TURKISH
- ZULU

BRAINSNACK® Number Block

Which number should replace the question mark?

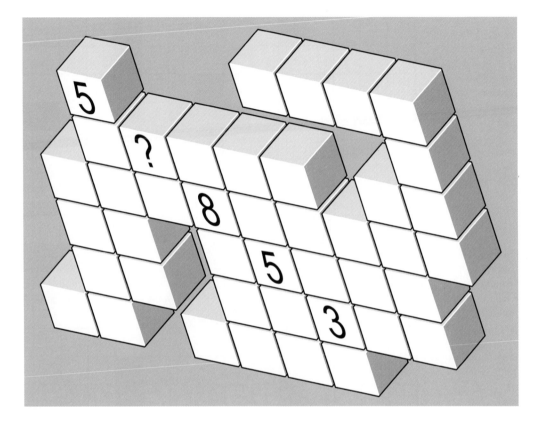

END GAME

The words you are seeking all have the letters END in them in the position indicated.
When you have found all of the answers, with help from the clues on the right, one column will
reveal the END GAME word, which radiates.

			E	**N**	**D**			Riser
___	___	___	**E**	**N**	**D**	___	___	Riser
___	___	___	**E**	**N**	**D**	___	___	Straightened
___	___	___	**E**	**N**	**D**	___	___	Repaired again
___	___	**E**	**N**	**D**	___	___	___	Much improving

Case Crackers

ACROSS

1 Narcissus spurned her
5 Palmer in *Moll Flanders*
10 Asset at Squaw Valley
14 Action-painting technique
15 *Gone With the Wind* actress Barbara
16 Tibetan monk
17 John Dickson Carr sleuth
19 Adam's grandson
20 Explorer Vespucci
21 Jean-Claude Van Damme film
23 Second vendition
24 Jimmy Carter's alma mater
25 Graceful seabird
27 Cause of yawning
30 More competent
33 *American Psycho* author
35 Sara of *Eastwick*
36 Where grass roots
37 Adduced
38 Waistcoat
39 Vichy water
40 Cargo bays
41 Mature efts
42 Catholicon
44 Aim at the barcode
46 Bittersweet covering
47 Orator
51 West Indies resorts
54 Bullish
55 Son of Ares
56 Erle Stanley Gardner sleuth
58 Aswan Dam locale
59 Japanese electronics company
60 A big person may come down with it
61 Ashe Stadium units
62 Joel Coen's brother
63 Auricles

DOWN

1 Mystery writer's award
2 Part of *CSI*
3 Animal skins
4 Runs
5 More protracted
6 The lowdown
7 Marvin in *The Dirty Dozen*
8 Air
9 Crystal Lake locale
10 45 cover
11 Carolyn Keene sleuth
12 *Typee* continuation
13 Narrow-waisted insect
18 Edmonton skater
22 Olympus Mons locale
26 *District 9* director Blomkamp
27 "God ___ America"
28 Remove from office
29 Citi Field nine
30 Baldwin in *The Aviator*
31 Boyfriend
32 *Remington Steele* sleuth
34 Inc. relative
37 Blow a big lead
38 Idolize
40 *License to Drive* star Corey
41 A Minor Prophet
43 Strikes out
45 Binney & Smith colorer
48 Campbell of *Martin*
49 "___ Own" (Bobby Brown hit)
50 Divides
51 Blue and Cross
52 "Acoustic Soul" singer India.___
53 Bench
54 "___ Little Tenderness"
57 Abbrev. after Sen. Ayotte's name

Kakuro

Each number in a black area is the sum of the numbers that you have to enter in the next empty boxes. The empty boxes that make up the sum are called a run. The sum of the across run is written above the diagonal in the black area and the sum of the down run is written below the diagonal. Runs can only contain the numbers 1 through 9 and each number in a run can only be used once. The gray boxes only contain odd numbers and the white only even numbers.

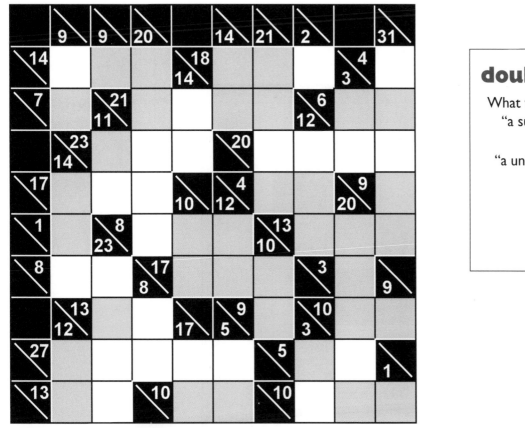

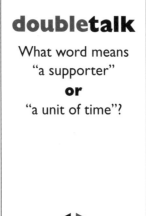

doubletalk

What word means
"a supporter"
or
"a unit of time"?

◄ ►

MISSING LETTER PROVERB

Fill in each missing letter, indicated by an X, to make a well-known proverb.

XAXKING XOXS XELXOM XITX

Keep Going

Start on a blank square of your choice and connect as many blank squares as possible with one single continuous line. You can only connect squares along vertical and horizontal lines, not along diagonal lines. You must continue the connecting line up until the next obstacle, i.e., the rim of the box, a black square or a square that has already been used. You can change direction at any obstacle you meet. Each square can only be used once. The number of blank squares that will be left unused is marked in the upper square. There is more than one solution. We only show one solution.

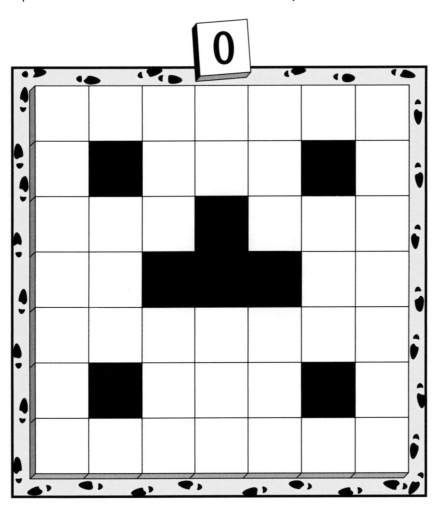

CROSSWORD Spanning the Spectrum

ACROSS

- **1** A purplish hue
- **5** Superman, for one
- **9** Game or program for an iPad, for short
- **12** Common fish for a sandwich
- **13** Not under
- **14** What cats shed
- **15** Highly excited
- **16** Color of a blue gem
- **18** Paradise
- **20** "A ___ of a different color"
- **21** Outer layer of the eye
- **24** Shiny fabric
- **25** Lessen
- **26** Beige
- **27** One of Columbus's ships
- **28** Candle material
- **29** Potato snack
- **33** 29 Down synonym
- **34** Support
- **35** Overseas
- **39** Restaurant employee
- **40** It secretes hormones
- **41** Wander
- **42** Color similar to lilac
- **44** Singer Bareilles
- **48** Prior to
- **49** Long time periods
- **50** Baker's need
- **51** Perfect number
- **52** Word before canal or vegetable
- **53** Dark blue shade

DOWN

- **1** School org.
- **2** Tote
- **3** Kids' card game
- **4** Color similar to fuchsia
- **5** Book of the Old Testament
- **6** ___ Almighty
- **7** Agent (abbrev.)
- **8** Parentless child
- **9** Blazing
- **10** Handbag
- **11** Primp
- **17** Spicy
- **19** Actress Sandra
- **21** Trash receptacle
- **22** ___-Wan Kenobi
- **23** Jogged
- **24** Branford Marsalis's instrument
- **26** A small bit
- **28** Married
- **29** Scarlet
- **30** Cap
- **31** Cube in your drink
- **32** Each
- **33** Comedian Gilda
- **34** Sheep's cry
- **35** Shoelace end
- **36** Blast
- **37** Black bird
- **38** Single
- **39** Most awful
- **41** Nevada city
- **43** ___-wop
- **45** Actress Gardner
- **46** Gun the engine
- **47** At ___ price

Color Travels

These mazes are a test of color perception as well as sense of direction. You may only travel from a pink block to a yellow one, from a yellow block to a blue one, from a blue block to a green one, and from a green block to a pink one on your way to the destination.

DISCO LIGHTS

Cross the bridge maze from bottom to top. You do not have to start at a pink square, but you must follow the correct color sequence. Diagonal moves are not allowed.

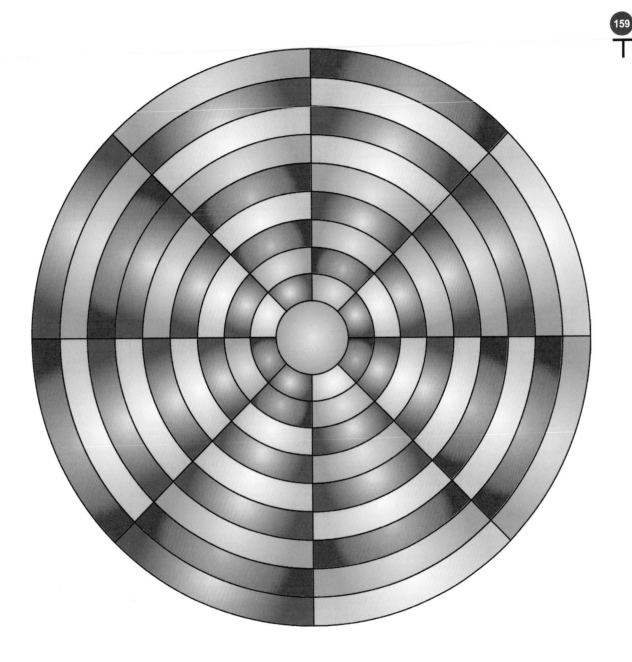

KALEIDOMAZE
Travel to the center from
any point outside the circle,
following the rules.

Doctor Who

ACROSS

1 "Spark" singer Tori
5 Three-horse open sleigh
11 Item in an ICU
14 Marsh bird
15 King of Morocco (1961–1999)
16 Merkel in *The Mad Doctor of Market Street*
17 Dr. Mark Craig's hospital, familiarly
19 Country legend Acuff
20 Ultra-ultra
21 Miami Heat home
22 *"My Way"* lyricist
23 Dog food brand
25 Takes the lead?
27 Mary Shelley's doctor
31 Hospital staffer
32 Slimy stuff
33 Over half of Israel
37 Balin in *The Young Doctors*
38 *ER* wardrobe item
41 Mystifier Geller
42 Rival of Paris
44 Sunflower state: Abbrev.
45 Champions Tour members
46 Misanthropic TV doctor
50 Lettuce variety
53 It's found in bars
54 "Alphabet Song" start
55 Saying
57 Southern Cal mascot
61 Push-up muscle
62 Russian doctor of fiction
64 Bar opening?
65 Crème ___
66 Eternally
67 She played Dr. Breene on *Third Watch*
68 Founder of modern astronomy
69 ___ avis

DOWN

1 Adjutant: Abbrev.
2 Sleuth played by Lorre
3 "Milk's favorite cookie"
4 Soup cracker
5 "I am the Alpha and ___": Rev. 1:8
6 Like sushi tuna
7 Dept. of Labor arm
8 "Oh, East ___, and West is West ..."
9 Tae kwon do's kin
10 Suffix for prop
11 *M*A*S*H* doctor
12 Gourmet mushroom
13 Rabbinic judge
18 Prepare beans
22 Obama cabineteer Duncan
24 Elitist
26 "Is so!" rebuttal
27 Inside the foul line
28 Left-leaning GOPer
29 Dr. Bricker on *The Love Boat*
30 "Boffo!"
34 Mentor
35 Psyche's lover
36 Workshop tool
38 Petty in *Free Willy*
39 Eight in a row?
40 "A rose by ___ name ...": Shak.
43 Falstaffian oath
45 Hollow roll
47 Safeguard
48 Get ready
49 Mata of espionage
50 Lickety-split
51 Like Mrs. Spratt
52 Capt. Kirk's doctor
56 "The doctor ___ see you now"
58 Starbucks quaff
59 Antiquing device
60 Ibsen's Helmer
62 H.S. publication
63 Zorro's mark

BRAINSNACK® Parking Space

Which car (1-11) is parked incorrectly?

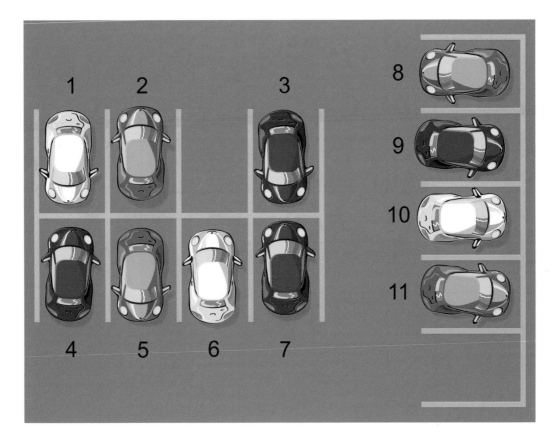

Put a letter in each of the squares below to make a word that means "mechanical devices."

These numbered clues refer to other words that can be made from the whole:

1 8 5 4 6 7 2 MASTER; 6 8 1 9 5 7 MEDDLE;
4 6 7 5 8 1 RIVER; 1 8 4 6 5 7 KEEPER.

1	2	3	4	5	6	7	8	9	10

Sudoku

Fill in the grid so that each row, each column and each 3 x 3 frame contains every number from 1 to 9.

	2							
				7	1	6		4
5		1	8				7	
3		2	9		7		8	
	4						3	
	7		6		3	2		9
	9				2	3		5
7		6	4	8				
							6	

do you KNOW?

Who wrote
The Pilgrim's Progress?

trivia • Which 19th-century English mathematician invented a 'difference engine' that anticipated the computer?

BRAINSNACK® Bright Lights

Which candle (A-F) will burn down first? The pink wax burns twice as long, and the green wax 3 times as long as the white wax.

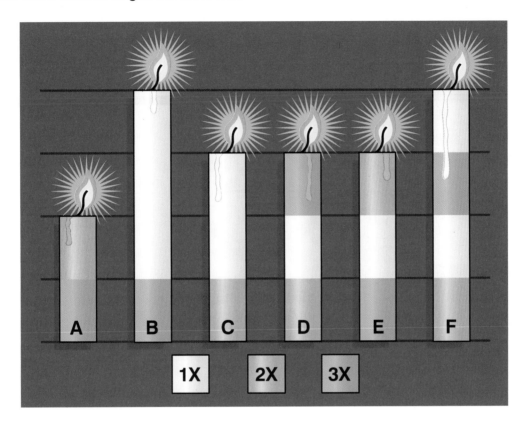

LETTER LINE

Put a letter in each of the squares below to make a word that means "restriction."

These numbered clues refer to other words that can be made from the whole:

1 7 6 5 2 9 4 BOXES;   1 2 3 5 6 7 4 5 DEGREE OF DIFFERENCE;
7 3 5 8 1 4 CAPERS; 10 8 3 10 HUE

1	2	3	4	5	6	7	8	9	10

BRAINSNACK® Flag It

Each signal flag is represented by a letter. Two signal flags strongly resemble each other per column. Which flag does not belong?

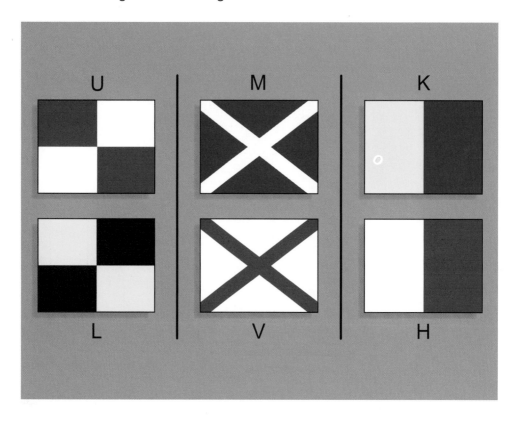

END GAME

The words you are seeking all have the letters END in them in the position indicated.
When you have found all of the answers, with help from the clues on the right, one column will reveal the END GAME word, which might take till the cows come home.

__	__	__	__	__	**E**	**N**	**D**	To protect or ward off
__	__	__	**E**	**N**	**D**	__	__	Disburser
__	__	__	**E**	**N**	**D**	__	__	A body of stories
E	**N**	**D**	__	__	__	__	__	Growth from within

CROSSWORD   On the Beach

ACROSS

1 PD broadcast
4 Deep purple
8 Mollusk associated with clue* answers
12 Extinct ostrich cousin
13 Milo in *Ulysses*
15 Burgundy river
16 Species
17 Paying*
19 Pesky critter, informally
21 Noncommittal words
22 *To Kill a Mockingbird* author Lee
23 2009 Dillinger portrayer
24 River of Wales
27 Richard Branson's title
28 SpongeBob's home
30 Joke around
32 "America's Puppet Master"
34 Walk off with
35 Father of Cainan
37 Sound judgment
39 Buzz Lightyear's owner
40 "With tears of innocency and terms ___": Shak.
42 Toyota sedan
44 Narcotics agcy.
45 London calamity of 1666
47 Code-breaking org.
49 Skywalker's friend
50 Eyes of a poet
51 Rung
54 General concept
55 Marine gastropods
56 Dummy*
60 Happening last mo.
61 Mark's successors
62 One of Homer's sisters-in-law
63 Highland turndown
64 *Armageddon* author Uris
65 Green veggies
66 Affront, to Ice-T

DOWN

1 *Witness* cast
2 Mazurka's kin
3 Thirteen rolls*
4 Lithographic works
5 Poe house
6 "Just Like Jesse James" singer
7 Spitchcock ingredient
8 Crafty
9 Card game with forfeits
10 Babylonian god
11 Yogi Berra, in 1973
14 Visitor to Earth
15 Threaten a bite
18 Discredit a witness
20 Fol ___ cheese
23 They work the graveyard shift?
24 No longer bedridden*
25 Glissade
26 Tanzania neighbor
28 Golf instructor
29 Book-sale gp.
30 Retirement plan name
31 Prefix for structure
33 ___ and clear (no strings attached)
36 Red or Dead
38 Motel freebie
41 Not seeing eye to eye
43 Turning Stone Casino tribe
46 Bridge supports
48 York or Pepper: Abbrev.
51 TV genre
52 Former Chinese premier Chou
53 Statesman Kefauver
54 Bettor's boast
55 Prompt beginning
56 *Snow White* frame
57 Tint
58 El Dorado treasure
59 With it

Sport Maze

Draw the shortest way from the ball to the goal. You can only move along vertical and horizontal lines, not along diagonal lines. The figure on each square indicates the number of squares the ball must be moved in the same direction. You can change direction at each stop.

1	5	3	4	4	4
1	2		4	2	1
4	3	3	1	4	4
4	2	1	3	4	2
1	2	4	3	1	4
2	1	5	4	1	2

change ONE

Change one letter in each of these two words to form a common two-word phrase from the field of sport.

FORK CUT

ONE LETTER LESS OR MORE

The word on the right side contains the letters of the word on the left side plus or minus the letter in the middle. One letter is already in the right place.

C A N O E I N G +R ☐ ☐ N ☐ ☐ ☐ ☐ ☐

WEATHER CHART **Sunny**

Where will the sun shine, if each arrow points in the direction of a spot where the symbol is located? The symbols cannot be next to each other vertically, horizontally or diagonally. A symbol cannot be placed on top of an arrow. We show one symbol.

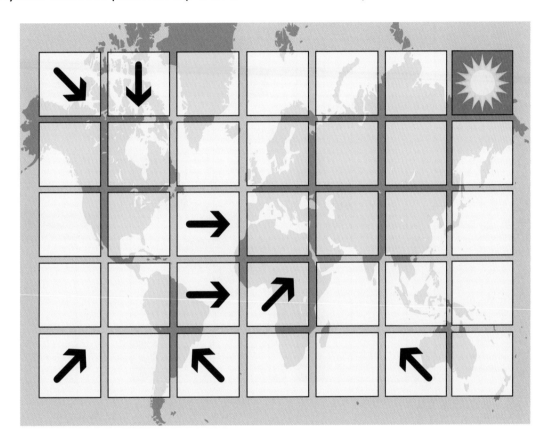

BLOCK ANAGRAM

Form the word that is described in the brackets with the letters above the grid. Extra letters are already in the right place.

RINGBIRD (board on collapsible supports)

Endangered Birds

ACROSS

1 Olympic Coven matriarch
5 Extant
10 First-grade studies
14 "How do you like ___ apples?"
15 Open to bribery
16 Ado
17 Endangered Central American raptor
19 Seethe
20 Orange grove
21 Edited film
23 "Oops! ... I Did It Again" singer
24 Potboiler writer
25 *Mikado* blade
27 Bayreuth locale
30 "Happy" singer Leona
33 Rainforest vine
35 Do sums
36 Wedding vows
37 Almost inadequate
38 Denver's altitude
39 Before this time
40 "Fields of Gold" singer
41 Ancient Greek physician
42 *Ordinary People* director
44 Egg on
46 Caterpillar hair
47 Kind of profiling
51 Motor City
54 "A dish best served cold"
55 Genus of swans
56 Endangered Australian raptor
58 *Slumdog Millionaire* costume
59 Lena in *Cabin in the Sky*
60 "Now I Know" singer White
61 BPOE members
62 Largest feline

63 King's *Faithful* collaborator

DOWN

1 Collective spirit
2 Musical symbol
3 Choreographer Cunningham
4 Accent
5 Unwilling
6 Stellar role
7 NYC Marathon sponsor
8 Kilmer and Avery
9 GOP symbol
10 Marungu sunbird's continent
11 Endangered marsh bird of Florida
12 Nicolas in *Ghost Rider*
13 Gunned it
18 "The one that got away" and others
22 *Dante's Peak* flow
26 *Cantar de Rodrigo* hero
27 Head locks
28 Wait at the light
29 Mideast gulf
30 Truth twister
31 Ford model
32 Endangered American wading bird
34 Scottish crime writer Rankin
37 A flush beats this
38 Mastroianni in *La Dolce Vita*
40 *Ice Age* sabertooth
41 Caribbean fruit
43 Big wheel of Paris
45 Have druthers
48 Like some Andean ruins
49 Israeli coin
50 Bolshevik leader
51 Rx amount
52 National airline of Israel
53 Picard's counselor
54 Hall-of-Famer Sandberg
57 0.0000001 joule

WORD SEARCH · Mathematics

All the words are hidden vertically, horizontally or diagonally—in both directions. The letters that remain unused form a sentence from left to right.

```
N  I  N  M  O  S  T  E  L  A  N  G  U  A  G
A  E  E  S  T  S  H  E  D  A  W  O  T  R  D
R  F  V  O  R  M  C  A  X  I  T  H  I  E  M
B  A  N  E  G  A  T  I  V  E  V  T  G  I  C
E  S  I  R  R  S  O  E  T  D  N  I  I  E  R
G  I  C  E  E  M  V  V  N  S  O  E  D  D  A
L  D  I  W  T  F  R  I  U  O  I  M  T  H  E
A  C  G  O  E  G  R  T  M  A  T  T  E  E  K
B  W  O  P  M  L  O  A  B  B  C  R  A  R  D
O  S  L  S  A  C  L  V  E  A  U  I  M  T  L
D  Á  U  T  I  H  I  I  R  C  D  A  N  A  S
Y  È  M  R  D  N  A  R  P  U  E  N  R  O  W
P  R  O  O  F  H  E  E  C  S  D  G  A  I  C
C  M  A  R  G  A  I  D  H  L  E  L  E  M  E
M  A  T  R  I  X  C  A  N  T  E  E  N  S  S
C  I  E  X  P  O  N  E  N  T  N  E  I  N  C
E  K  N  Y  T  I  N  I  F  N  I  O  L  W  L
E  D  G  E  O  R  L  E  A  R  L  N  I  N  G
```

- ABACUS
- ADD
- ALGEBRA
- AXIOM
- BODY
- CIRCLE
- CONIC
- COSINE
- DEDUCTION
- DERIVATIVE
- DIAGRAM
- DIAMETER
- DIGIT
- DIVIDE
- ELLIPSE
- EVEN
- EXPONENT
- INFINITY
- INTEGRAL
- LINE
- LINEAR
- LOGIC
- MATRIX
- NEGATIVE
- NUMBER
- POWER
- PROOF
- STATISTICS
- SURFACE
- TRIANGLE

Cage the Animals

Draw lines to completely divide up the grid into small squares with exactly one animal per square. The squares should not overlap.

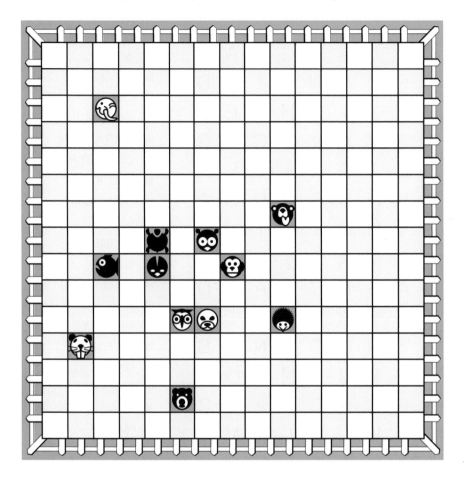

LETTERBLOCKS

Move the letterblocks around so that words are formed on top and below that you can associate with gardens.

WORD POWER **Science Diction**

Even if you're not the world's biggest science fiction fan,
you have to admit that it has given our lexicon some otherworldly words.
We celebrate the sci-fi genre—with some fact, folklore, and fantasy mixed in for good
measure. Strap in, space cowboys!

. . . .

1. grok *v.*—A: understand profoundly. B: stun, as with a gun. C: shed, as the coat of an animal.

2. psionic *adj.*—A: having paranormal ability. B: alive but frozen. C: synthetic.

3. Chimera *n.*—A: constellation named for Greek scholar. B: mythological monster. C: *Martian Chronicles* villain.

4. chrononaut *n.*—A: space traveler. B: pilot in orbit. C: time traveler.

5. draconic *adj.*—A: of or relating to a dragon. B: alien. C: cruel or severe.

6. sapient *adj.*—A: artificially alive. B: having characteristics of multiple animals. C: keen, discerning.

7. terraform *v.*—A: destroy with heat. B: alter an environment so it can support life. C: group similar species.

8. cryonics *n.*—A: practice of freezing a dead person in hopes of later restoring life. B: artificial intelligence. C: study of sea creatures.

9. lycanthropic *adj.*—of or relating to ... A: fairies. B: werewolves. C: celestial phenomena.

10. selenology *n.*—A: study of microorganisms. B: study of Greek gods. C: study of the moon.

11. dystopia *n.*—A: cosmic chaos. B: nightmarish society. C: underwater civilization.

12. android *n.*—A: robot with a human shape. B: robot with skin. C: human with robotic limbs.

13. cyborg *n.*—A: humanlike alien. B: robot with artificial intelligence. C: bionic human.

14. telluric *adj.*—A: of or relating to the earth. B: gifted with extrasensory perception. C: prone to exploding.

Tiny Circles

Round and round the maze does flow, find the center, off you go.
(Start at the arrow to the left of the maze.)

CROSSWORD # Endangered Mammals

ACROSS

1 Gefilte fish ingredient
5 Anchor position
10 Lift at Aspen
14 "Of course!"
15 "___ On, Harvest Moon"
16 Spanish stew
17 Endangered Chinese mammal
19 Destroy
20 Like groupies
21 Mason's secretary
23 Make good as new
24 Rod in the Hall of Fame
25 The night before
26 Castigated
29 Boxer Mosley
32 Head lines
33 Coors brew
34 Portion
35 President before Garfield
36 A flat, thick piece
37 Doll snap-on
38 Sharpened
39 Melt ore
40 Bony-plated fish
42 "Zip-a-Dee-___-Dah"
43 Trousseau
44 "___ Perfect": Miley Cyrus
48 Taiwan capital
50 Number of courts in Wimbledon
51 1965 Beatles album
52 Endangered African mammal
54 Stanley Gardner
55 "American Pie" destination
56 Prefix for derm
57 American-born Jordanian queen
58 Manicurist's board
59 Extinct

DOWN

1 Stogie
2 "All kidding ___ ..."
3 Enlarges a hole
4 Contrite
5 Aim for the stars
6 Title for Macbeth
7 Best man's concern
8 Terre Haute locale: Abbrev.
9 Kulaks
10 Tico of Bon Jovi
11 Endangered marine mammal
12 Shepard's ___ of the Mind
13 Dennis Miller specialty
18 Treasure hoard
22 Hall-of-Famer Speaker
24 100% again
26 Checkbook entry
27 Carrier to Jerusalem
28 Liability
29 Fat farms
30 ___ Krishna
31 Endangered bony-plated mammal
32 Abner Yokum's mammy
35 Awful
36 Ironed out
38 "Battle Hymn of the Republic" poet
39 On the wagon
41 Dennis in *Waterworld*
42 ___ Kong (early video game)
44 Better quality
45 Salt a street
46 Gossipmonger
47 Rosie the Riveter's hairnet
48 In which case
49 Prefix for sol
50 Approach to the altar
53 Moon module

Word Sudoku

Complete the grid so that each row, each column and each 3 x 3 frame contains the nine letters from the black box below. The hidden nine-letter word is in the diagonal from top left to bottom right.

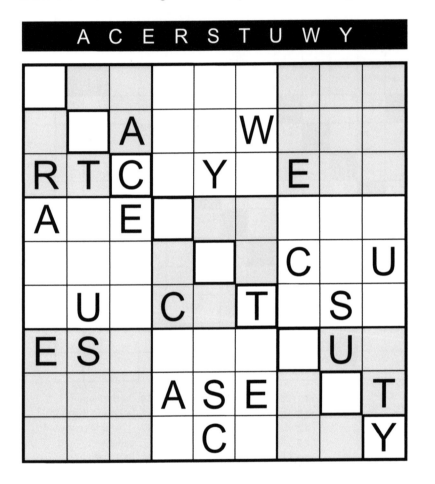

A C E R S T U W Y

TRANSADDITION

Add one letter to **STEW SIR?** and rearrange the rest to find a word with a connection to the original phrase.

_____

Spot the Differences

Find the nine differences in the image on the bottom right.

trivia

- What is the hottest country in the world?

do you KNOW?

How many sides does a dodecahedron have?

CROSSWORD · '50s Music Legends

ACROSS

1 Seed casings
5 Lessen
10 Picnic pests
14 Esprit
15 The _____ & the Papas
16 A drum keeps it
17 "Orinoco Flow" singer
18 "Johnny B. Goode" singer
20 Iridescent shell layer
22 Churn
23 *Fantastic Mr. _____*
24 King of Judea
27 Big city bane
29 Record label
31 Burden
33 "_____ the money" (2 words)
37 Flub
38 Slander
40 Not a comedy
41 Use eBay, maybe
43 He's left the building
45 Abbrev. in legal papers or literary citations
46 Perfect
48 Coke and Pepsi
50 Female
51 A bigger busybody
53 Take a nap
54 1981 film _____ *Boot*
55 Sketch
57 Horned animal
59 Word before limit or bracket
62 Fed. job safety org.
64 Caesar or Nero
67 "Peggy Sue" singer
71 Mute actor
72 Ordered
73 Aristocracy
74 Again
75 Singers Grant and Winehouse
76 Parts of saxophones
77 Puts on

DOWN

1 _____ there, done that
2 Arm bone
3 "Hit the Road Jack" singer
4 Type of drum
5 Theater gp.
6 _____ humbug
7 River between Russia and China
8 Mexican dish
9 Northern native
10 16th president's nickname
11 Toy football brand
12 Root veggie
13 "Come Sail Away" band
19 Pale yellow
21 Son of Aphrodite
25 A-ha song "Take_____" (2 words)
26 Games of swordplay
28 Actor Richard
29 Plastic
30 Statement of beliefs
32 Enjoy
34 "Blueberry Hill" singer
35 Nebraska city
36 Rattled breathing
39 Musician's list of hospitality requests
42 Placed
44 Belt
47 "Bad, Bad _____ Brown"
49 Mix
52 Amount of bacon
56 _____ wheat
58 Wanderer
59 "Dancing Queen" group
60 U.S. territory in the Pacific
61 Current
63 "I cannot tell _____" (2 words)
65 Prayer ender
66 Current events
68 _____ Moines
69 Abbrev. after a company name
70 Affirmative

Sudoku Twin

Fill in the grid so that each row, each column and each 3 x 3 frame contains
every number from 1 to 9. A sudoku twin is two connected 9 x 9 sudokus.

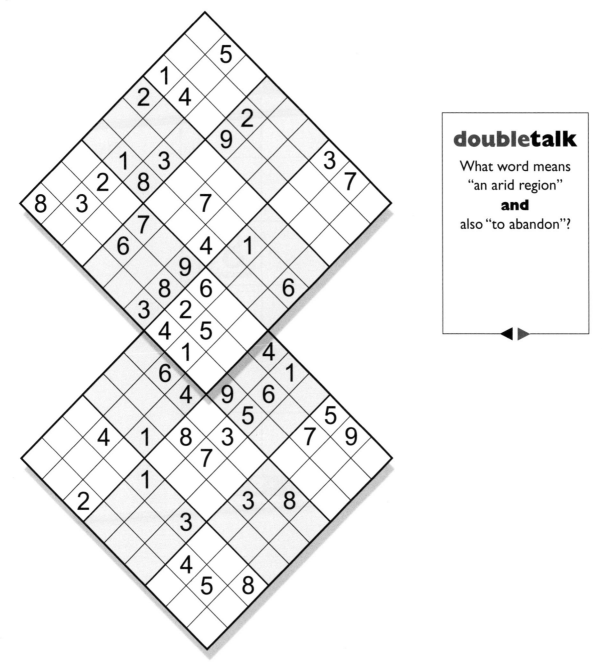

doubletalk

What word means
"an arid region"
and
also "to abandon"?

Number Cluster

Cubes showing numbers have been placed on the grid below with some spaces left empty. Can you complete the grid by creating runs of the same number and of the same length as the number? So where a cube with number 5 has been included on the grid you need to create a run of five number 5's, including the cube already shown. The run can be horizontal, vertical or both horizontal and vertical.

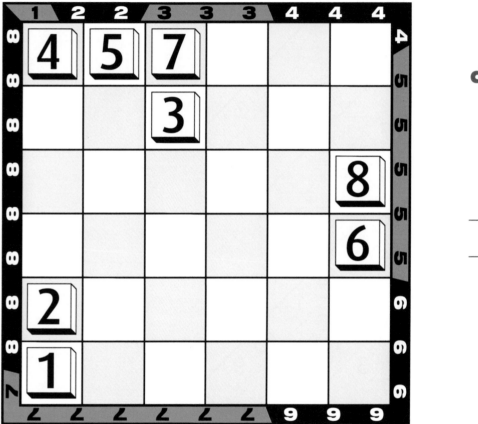

do you KNOW?

How many pieces are there in a standard set of dominoes?

_____

_____

MISSING LETTER PROVERB

Fill in each missing letter, indicated by an X, to make a well-known proverb.

XLX XOOX XXINXS MXST XOME XO AX XND

Sudoku

Fill in the grid so that each row, each column and each 3 x 3 frame contains every number from 1 to 9.

5					9	2		
		4		2				1
	7		4				3	8
		8	2	5				9
	3						4	
2				4	3	8		
8	6				7		2	
3				8		1		
		1	6					3

trivia

- Which two countries' names include the letter 'x'?

---

do you KNOW ● What the University of Paris is known as?

Letter Search #3

In the grid below, find all appearances of the letter K, both capital and lowercase, any color. When you are ready, set a stopwatch or note the time. Circle every letter K. Then go back and count how many appear in capital and how many in lowercase. Finally, count how many Ks appear in **green**. Note how long it took you, and see if you can beat your time in the other letter searches.

FOR THIS EXERCISE, YOU'LL NEED:
A pen or pencil • A stopwatch or watch or clock with a second hand

K	a	N	M	r	r	N	c	N	m	n	k	A	r	X	c	X	m	x	r	N	a
k	R	n	n	r	k	r	X	B	k	k	M	z	N	r	n	k	r	X	N	Z	N
a	x	m	Z	r	R	r	K	Z	N	X	k	R	X	n	k	k	n	R	a	k	X
x	r	x	n	Z	k	m	X	R	r	Z	c	m	x	Z	r	Z	m	X	Z	r	R
m	Z	c	Z	N	a	Z	n	Z	R	m	N	r	R	M	z	A	Z	m	c	k	R
R	m	z	n	X	r	Z	m	N	K	z	x	N	a	z	R	z	M	r	z	X	r
X	z	N	k	m	M	c	z	Z	r	c	X	R	N	n	z	K	R	a	K	k	n
c	m	z	R	z	k	c	M	N	Z	x	m	z	B	a	x	X	M	R	X	m	m
x	X	N	z	m	r	R	x	A	X	n	z	m	Z	X	N	z	M	n	X	a	X
n	X	A	k	r	n	m	x	R	a	X	R	R	r	m	c	R	n	B	a	k	z
k	x	z	M	Z	k	N	z	m	R	N	X	a	k	r	R	x	r	k	X	r	X
B	Z	r	X	r	K	a	Z	B	z	R	z	N	A	K	M	x	X	c	R	n	A
r	X	n	x	a	R	M	k	k	Z	x	r	X	k	a	c	K	x	R	n	R	z
c	x	z	N	R	x	c	M	m	R	n	z	B	M	x	R	z	n	R	z	x	M
N	R	r	R	z	r	R	n	Z	R	n	m	R	A	a	X	X	r	m	R	n	Z
R	z	R	z	N	z	B	x	R	R	r	Z	x	R	n	X	a	z	m	R	x	n
k	R	n	n	r	k	r	X	B	k	k	M	z	N	r	n	k	r	X	N	Z	N
B	Z	r	X	k	K	a	Z	B	z	K	z	N	A	k	M	x	X	c	R	n	A
q	X	N	z	m	r	R	x	A	X	n	z	w	Z	X	K	z	p	n	X	a	Z

TIME _____   NUMBER OF CAPITAL Ks_____

NUMBER OF LOWERCASE Ks_____   NUMBER OF GREEN Ks_____

CROSSWORD Festivities

ACROSS

1 Ditzy
6 Slaves of yore
11 Lotion letters
14 "I bid you ___"
15 Valerie Harper sitcom
16 Before, in verse
17 Go up in smoke
19 Section of LA
20 Centennial lead-in
21 Furthermore
22 Most proximate
24 Beach
27 Rocker Ocasek
28 Affectedly creative
33 Vanzetti's codefendant
36 Bolt a torpedo
37 Thompson in *Wit*
38 Cambridge cathedral city
39 Sings like a bird
43 Atmosphere: Comb. form
44 Mile, e.g.
46 ___ Fighters (rock group)
47 Fine-tuned
49 News promo catchphrase
53 Owner of Abbey Road Studios
54 Aerie locales
58 Traduce
62 Torn or tear
63 Sozzled
64 Runnymede, for one
65 Entertain lavishly
68 Emulate Hanks
69 Flash Gordon's sidekick
70 Ripley's "Believe It ___!"
71 Final degree
72 Product
73 Squalls

DOWN

1 Gentle breezes
2 Town near Limerick
3 Protozoan propellers
4 Mitchell in *Good Burger*
5 Win a pitchers' duel
6 Howlers
7 HBO rival
8 Horse or cow, e.g.
9 Margin
10 *The English Patient* locale
11 New England town officer
12 They play for pay
13 Word that can follow the starts of clue answers
18 Cowboy Gibson
23 Plentiful
25 Oklahoma tribe
26 Hardware store purchase
29 Long Beach loc.
30 Road-atlas abbrev.
31 Neverland pirate
32 Sale site
33 Bondservant
34 Jai follower
35 Bike lane
40 Toward the rear
41 Future perch?
42 Border collie
45 Aare tributary
48 Toronto loc.
50 Plane lane
51 Gofer's mission
52 Artery
55 Golfers Dutra and Browne
56 ___ noir wine
57 Cancels a cancellation
58 Rickman of *Harry Potter* films
59 Faction
60 iPhone "virtual assistant" app
61 *The Neverending Story* author
66 Grig
67 Soul group ___ Hill

WORD SEARCH **Biology**

All the words are hidden vertically, horizontally or diagonally—in both directions. The letters that remain unused form a sentence from left to right.

```
B S I O E S U G N U F L S O G
Y C I S R A N K E X A G C T S
C I A F O I E I N C N E T H A
T T I O V C S N S I S O M S O
S E R S I E T S R Y L I M A F
D N E S N L U H Y M O T A N A
O E T I M L T I L U N G S I D
P G C L O W I P E S L I V T I
O E A N O A E S U A P O N E M
R R B R G L C R B E A T U R R
H O G E S L F E N D I O X I N
T V O R M L O E R E F L E X E
R I S O A M L N O I T A T U M
A N I M A L S P E C I E S F L
I R M F O O R G A N I S M E A
T A D P O L E N D S I I G N S
M C O F L E C N A T S I S E R
I F T A T I B A H E C Y C L E
```

- AMOEBA
- ANATOMY
- ANIMAL SPECIES
- ARTHROPODS
- BACTERIA
- CARNIVORE
- CELL WALL
- CYCLE
- DIOXIN
- FAMILY
- FOSSIL
- FUNGUS
- GENETICS
- GROWTH RINGS
- HABITAT
- KINSHIP
- LUNGS
- MAMMAL
- MENOPAUSE
- MUTATION
- OMNIVORE
- ORGANISM
- OSMOSIS
- POLLEN
- REFLEX
- RESISTANCE
- RETINA
- TADPOLE
- TISSUE

Keep Going

Start on a blank square of your choice and connect as many blank squares as possible with one single continuous line. You can only connect squares along vertical and horizontal lines, not along diagonal lines. You must continue the connecting line up until the next obstacle, i.e., the rim of the box, a black square or a square that has already been used. You can change direction at any obstacle you meet. Each square can only be used once. The number of blank squares that will be left unused is marked in the upper square. There is more than one solution. We only show one solution.

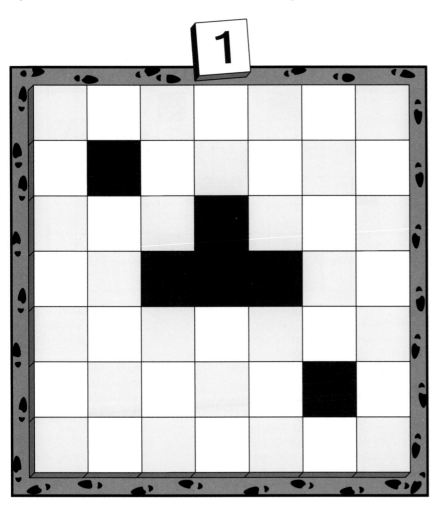

CROSSWORD **Sea Shanties**

ACROSS

1 Muslim pilgrimage
5 Foot rest
9 *You Can't Go Home Again* author
14 Arab father
15 Julie's *Dr. Zhivago* costar
16 Iroquois tribesmen
17 Sea shanty variant of "Spanish Ladies"
20 Dutch master
21 *Titus Andronicus* auth.
22 Inn drink
23 Afrikaner
26 Zone
28 Shanty about the Black Ball Line
34 Cereal for kids
35 Oswego or oolong
36 Dawdle
37 Thousand Islands island
38 Breakwaters
41 Abel's mom
42 Roshan Seth's *Gandhi* role
44 Photo order: Abbrev.
45 Cubist Mondrian
46 1840 shanty about whaling
50 Cargo pallet
51 Puppy chatter
52 Fabergé collectible
55 G-men
57 "___ a dream ...": King
61 Shanty also known as "A-Rovin' "
65 Dome home
66 Slight
67 Topple from power
68 Put on board
69 Graceful bird
70 GPA spoilers

DOWN

1 Does some field work
2 Like ___ out of hell
3 Completed
4 Kind of stage musical
5 Future fry
6 John L. Lewis's org.
7 Slangy denials
8 Heather in *The Hangover*
9 Some are three-day
10 Boston Bruin legend
11 Broad bean
12 Natural ability
13 Puzzle slave
18 Sufficient, to Shelley
19 Video game heroine Croft
24 Sermon ending?
25 Orator's skill: Abbrev.
27 Citrus cooler
28 Pipe plant
29 Like belly dancers
30 Down the hatch
31 Liquid glyceride
32 Bid adieu, from the window
33 Vladimir's refusal
34 Zesty flavor
38 Chips and dips, e.g.
39 Long race, for short
40 Italian island
43 Thing, in legalese
45 Kind of car engine
47 Readily
48 Morticia's family
49 Early Howard role
52 Pianist Gilels
53 Lady of glam rock
54 Apply gold leaf
56 Merganser
58 Together, musically
59 Phlox holder
60 911 respondents
62 A deer, a female deer
63 Span. matron
64 Julie Andrews film

BRAINSNACK® **Cubism**

Which group of cubes (1-5) does not belong?

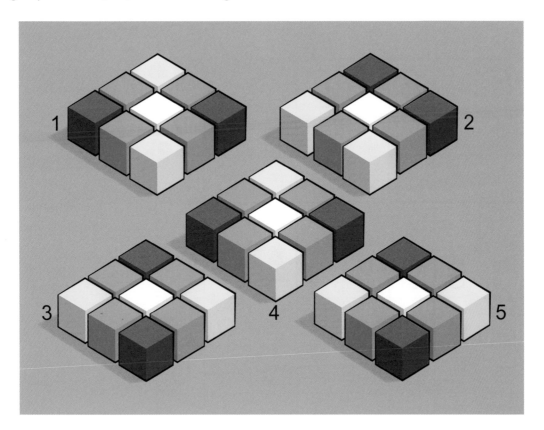

LETTER LINE

Put a letter in each of the squares below to make a word that means "to present or announce."

These numbered clues refer to other words that can be made from the whole:

4 9 6 7 8 3 1 5 2 MONEY OFF; 1 2 6 7 8 9 PERSUADE;
8 5 2 6 7 1 3 PASSAGE; 4 7 1 2 9 6 DESTROYED

1	2	3	4	5	6	7	8	9

Sudoku X

Fill in the grid so that each row, each column and each 3 x 3 frame contains every number from 1 to 9. The two main diagonals of the grid also contain every number from 1 to 9.

9	5	4	8	7	6		3	
	1					6	4	7
2							5	
7				2				8
5	8	6	9	3		4		
	3	7				6		
				7	5			6
			4					
		8						

do you KNOW

In the TV comedy series *Frasier*, what is Frasier's surname?

_____

_____

WORD SEARCH Cars

All the words are hidden vertically, horizontally or diagonally—in both directions. The letters that remain unused form a sentence from left to right.

```
R I N C R D R A O B H S A D N
O E T A R S B U M P E R I N O
O W H E E L L G L G N I N U T
D H G Y D Y E S T R T R I M S
I E I D N S S C T E R U O E I
N E L O I V E C O U P É R H P
I L E B L N I K R C R O N B P
M S K E Y N D T A O L H A E O
L L A A C G W I T R A U D S F
M I R R O R A A C N B A T O R
C E B C A R I B D A L C M C A
N U F A C D T L R S T O U R H
E R S T A O E L O I O O K F O
S P A R K P L U G R A L R A L
T E R N A S T L E B T A E S T
I V T A E S K C A B E N S O U
R P M A L G O F C E S T O F E
N E T H E A D L I G H T R G Y
```

- AIRBAG
- BACK SEAT
- BODY
- BRAKE LIGHT
- BRAKES
- BUMPER
- CLUTCH
- COOLANT
- COUPÉ
- CYLINDER
- DASHBOARD
- DIESEL
- DOOR
- FOG LAMP
- HANDLE
- HEADLIGHT
- HORN
- INDICATORS
- MIRROR
- PEDALS
- PISTON
- RADIATOR
- RIMS
- SEAT
- SEAT BELT
- SPARK PLUG
- TUNING
- TURBO
- WHEEL
- WHEELS

BRAINSNACK® Odd Number

Which number does not belong?

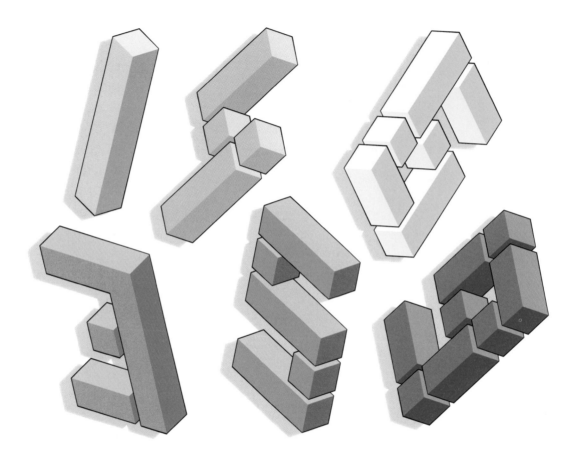

DOODLE PUZZLE

A doodle puzzle is a combination of images, letters and/or numbers that represent a word or a concept. If you cannot solve a doodle puzzle, do not look at the answer right away. Think hard—and outside the box.

TRIVIAL PURSUIT **1967**

As hippies came of age in the Summer of Love,
their music reflected the creativity and experimentation that went along with social
upheaval. Rock lovers look back on '67 as a banner year, when fresh voices and veteran
musicians exploded expectations with brave new sounds.

DO YOU KNOW THESE NOW-ICONIC LPS AND THEIR ARTISTS?

1 The debut album by the son of a protest singer of the '30s and '40s featured an 18-minute title track about a diner.

2 The debut by an unparalleled American guitarist included a hit penned, mostly in haste, backstage at a London nightclub.

3 Another debut, this self-titled album had a beloved anthem about, in part, a girl's complexion.

4 This album by a British blues band, above, had a power hit punctuated by massive guitar fuzz inspired by Jimi Hendrix.

5 This self-titled debut was a jazz-influenced frenzy led by a furious poet who urged listeners to "Light My Fire."

6 This album had two big hits, one about finding love "when the truth is found to be lies," the other a psychedelic interpretation of *Alice in Wonderland*.

TEST YOUR RECALL

What car was produced from 1967 to 2002 with the characteristic "Coke bottle" styling?

Best-Sellers #2

ACROSS

1 Poor golf shot
5 First Family daughter
10 Wasteland
14 Three oceans touch it
15 Jordan capital
16 "You ___": Lady Gaga
17 Nora Roberts best-seller
19 Jockey's strap
20 Balance providers
21 Decent, so to speak
23 Salad green
24 *From Here to Eternity* island
25 *The Water Horse* loch
27 Folic acid, for one
30 Rough finish
33 2000 election hangers
35 Jane Smiley best-seller
36 You've heard this before
37 Harvests
38 Head of France
39 Notice
40 Fauvist Matisse
41 Sea fan
42 1946 Triple Crown horse
44 Beat bad
46 Sea eagle
47 Kind of energy
51 Henry Fonda western (with *The*)
54 Pizza spice
55 As far as
56 Elin Hilderbrand best-seller
58 "___ to Run": Springsteen
59 Online letter
60 Work without ___ (risk it)
61 Ice-cream brand
62 "My Heart Belongs to ___"
63 Beatty and Flanders

DOWN

1 Juice the goose
2 Colorado ski spot
3 Kind of hockey
4 ___ line (conform)
5 Buffalo team
6 "Girl" singer Tori
7 Dallas school
8 Worker
9 Robots
10 *Nick of Time* actress Mason
11 David Baldacci best-seller
12 *Garfield* canine
13 Peel
18 "American Pie" destination
22 Café sign
26 Perfume
27 Bland
28 9th Greek letter
29 "Away in a Manger" is one
30 Rimrock
31 Gets a serve past
32 Robert Crais best-seller
34 Laughter sound
37 Allowed to go
38 Bobsled relative
40 Track down
41 More adorable
43 Illegal ignitions
45 Almost never
48 Boothbay Harbor locale
49 "Lady ___": Chris de Burgh
50 Indianapolis team
51 London subway
52 Apple product
53 *Green Mansions* girl
54 *Amores* poet
57 Schoolboy

Word Sudoku

Complete the grid so that each row, each column and each 3 x 3 frame contains the nine letters from the black box below. The hidden nine-letter word is in the diagonal from top left to bottom right.

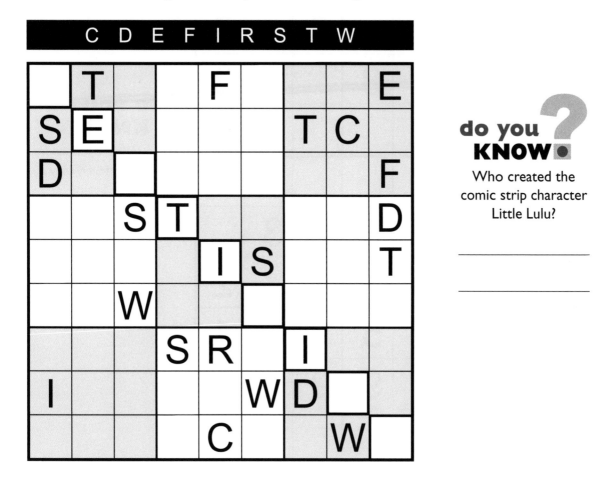

C D E F I R S T W

do you KNOW?

Who created the comic strip character Little Lulu?

_____

_____

UNCANNY TURN

Rearrange the letters of the phrase to form a cognate anagram, one that is related or connected in meaning to the original phrase. The answer can be one or more words.

TRY HERO PART

Sudoku

Fill in the grid so that each row, each column and each 3 x 3 frame contains every number from 1 to 9.

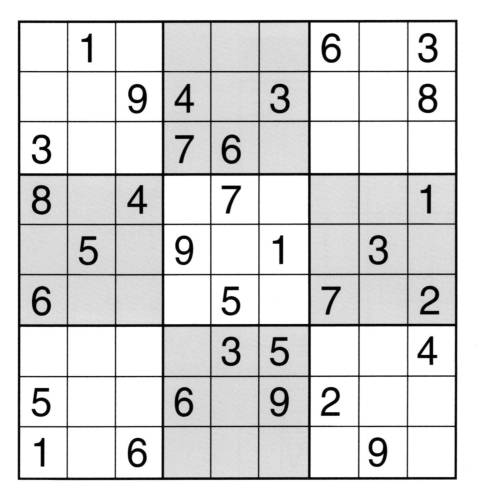

triVia • What do astronomers call the point directly overhead in the sky?

CROSSWORD # Stargazing

ACROSS

1 Aug. 31, 2012, hosted a Blue ___
5 Cushion
8 Star that is part of the Summer Triangle
12 College in Southern California
13 "On the ___ hand..."
14 Hit a hole-in-one
15 Thin wooden wedge
16 Business abbreviation
17 Chilly
18 Relating to music written in a particular key
20 Gumbo veggie
22 Involuntary spasm
24 Ringed planet, in the west after sunset in August 2012
28 Constellation named for a mythic king
32 Creepy
33 ___ de Janeiro
34 Run-of-___-mill
36 Report card stat
37 Proper contraction for "ain't"
40 September 2012 featured the ___ Moon
43 The Perseid ___ shower occurs every August
45 Football kicker's need
46 Turn sharply
48 Nonchalant
52 Location
55 Not many
57 Type of stringed instrument
58 Hospital section
59 Opposite WSW
60 Russian mountain range
61 Constellation home to 8 Across

62 ___ and reel
63 The red planet, also in the west after sunset in August 2012

DOWN

1 Has to
2 Eight, in Spanish
3 Actress Lena
4 Quarterback "Broadway Joe"
5 Hawaiian food
6 ___ domini (A.D.)
7 Patios
8 Clear out
9 Novelist Umberto
10 Hair product
11 Put one and one together
19 Fib
21 *Norma* ___
23 Slice
25 Desire
26 Tears
27 Tidy
28 Stuff
29 Ireland
30 Writer of verse
31 Hushing sound
35 Dine

38 State of 47 Down
39 Peep-___ sandal
41 Confederate soldier
42 Wedding invite paper
44 Mention
47 Gambling city
49 Glow
50 Our sun is one
51 Slithery swimmers
52 Hole-making device
53 Beam of sunshine
54 Flub
56 Marry

Pentathlon

These challenges are a mix of logic, spatial awareness, technical reasoning, arithmetic, and visual acuity. They are a kind of pentathlon that you do in your own armchair.

EASY READING

In how many ways can the word EASY be read? Start at the central letter E and move to an adjacent letter up, down, backward, or forward, in and out in any direction.

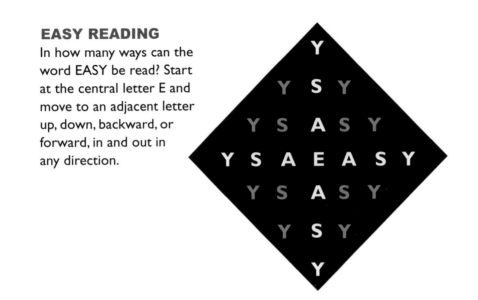

ONE INTO TWO

By using just one cut, divide this figure into two identical shapes.

DICE TOWER

Four dice are stacked one on top of the other. What is the total value of the three pairs of hidden faces in the stack, given that the top face is a 6 and the bottom face is a 3?

1

2

3

4

UNFINISHED WORK

How many more blocks are needed to turn this incomplete construction into a solid cube, assuming that all blocks are the same size as those already placed and that none of the blocks already placed is moved?

UPHILL STRUGGLE

When you push an object up a slope, in which of the four directions shown is the load?

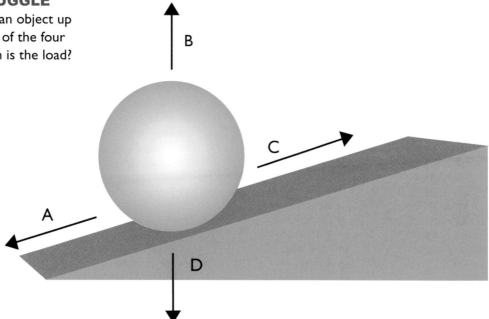

Relaxation

ACROSS

1 Scored 1 at Sawgrass
5 Like Presley's early records
9 *Enola Gay* cargo
14 Petty in *Free Willy*
15 Auction site
16 Gaffer's milieu
17 First element of a perfect summer's day
20 Gibson garnish
21 ___ loss for words
22 Juice bar orders
23 Itch
26 All tied
28 Second element of a perfect summer's day
33 Some are liberal
34 Astral altar
35 Superman, on Krypton
37 Super Sunday shout
38 Hickman and Johnson
41 *Die Fledermaus* role
42 Kunta of *Roots*
44 "Star Spangled Banner" preposition
45 Wolf relatives
46 Third element of a perfect summer's day
50 Concept
51 Gumbo pod
52 Richard in *Gog*
55 Vex
57 Single-celled protozoan
61 Fourth element of a perfect summer's day
65 Niger's neighbor
66 Of the ear
67 Patricia in *Hud*
68 Like Splenda
69 "Here ___ again!"
70 James Bond foe

DOWN

1 A chorus line
2 Joe McCarthy's counsel
3 "Able was I ___ ..."
4 Cuts out of the will
5 Game pieces
6 Japanese sash
7 *Pioneer 10* org.
8 Bluepoint
9 Cannes chum
10 Mother lode
11 "Ibis" poet
12 Tunnel
13 Panhandles
18 The U of CPU
19 One not in need
24 Deli salad
25 Greek Juno
27 Cries in balloons
28 Galahad's quest
29 Culture: Comb. form
30 Sluggish inlet
31 G-man Ness
32 Rushlike
33 Ham's refuge
36 ___ Palmas
38 Legal paper
39 Pixar clownfish
40 Composer Satie
43 Hostess snack cake
45 April birthstone
47 Bridle attachment
48 Jean in *Bombshell*
49 Apothecary's weight
52 Recedes
53 Escalated
54 Superb
56 Winslet in *Contagion*
58 Pitcher
59 Noodle
60 1968 folk album
62 "Say ah" clinic
63 Censure
64 Sarge

Word Pyramid

Each word in the pyramid has the letters of the word above it, plus a new letter.

A

(1) Babylonian god of wisdom
(2) large body of salt water
(3) occasion for buying at reduced prices
(4) rent
(5) benumbed
(6) get worse
(7) delight

do you KNOW?

What kind of creature is a Bombay Duck?

_____

_____

Word Ladders

In a word ladder puzzle, you have to change one word into another by altering a single letter at each step. Each step on the word ladder must be a valid word. This type of puzzle was invented in 1878 by Lewis Carroll, the author of *Alice in Wonderland*.

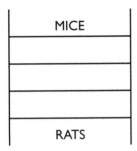

WORD LADDER 1
Turn MICE into RATS
1 Small creature
2 Win at chess
3 Floor coverings

WORD LADDER 3
Turn FOOL into SAGE
1 Common fund
2 Number of votes cast
3 Become wearisome
4 Wan
5 Attendant

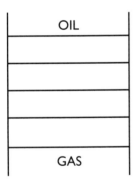

WORD LADDER 2
Turn OIL into GAS
1 Nothing
2 Pinch
3 Doze
4 Aperture

WORD LADDER 4
Turn TEARS into SMILE
1 Scorches
2 Heavenly bodies
3 Look fixedly
4 No longer fresh
5 Steps for climbing over a wall

In the examples below we've taken out the clues to make it a little more difficult.

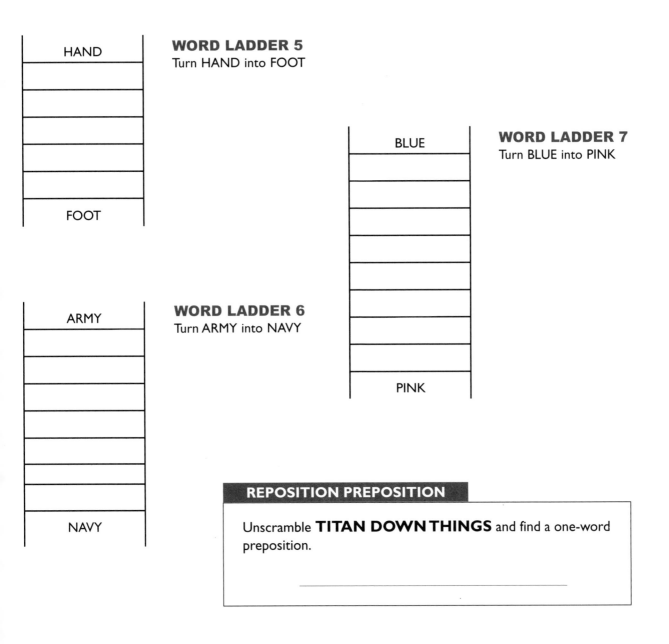

HAND
FOOT

WORD LADDER 5
Turn HAND into FOOT

BLUE
PINK

WORD LADDER 7
Turn BLUE into PINK

ARMY
NAVY

WORD LADDER 6
Turn ARMY into NAVY

REPOSITION PREPOSITION

Unscramble **TITAN DOWN THINGS** and find a one-word preposition.

_____

Binairo

Complete the grid with zeros and ones until there are 6 zeros and 6 ones in every row and every column. No more than two of the same number can be next to or under each other. Rows or columns with exactly the same content are not allowed. There is only one valid solution.

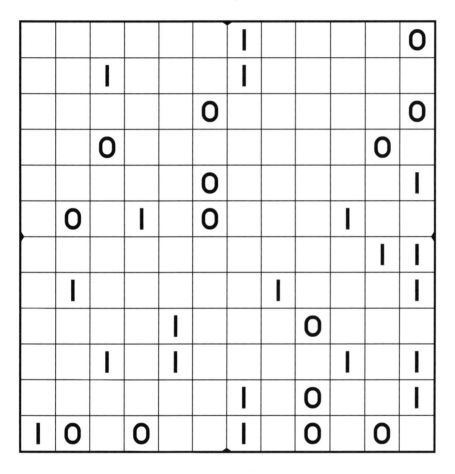

do you KNOW

What tennis star was stabbed in a match in the '90s?

_____

_____

REPOSITION PREPOSITION

Unscramble **RID OF SAME** and find a two-word preposition.

_____

CROSSWORD **First Name Last**

ACROSS

1 Breakfast order
5 Alaskan salmon
9 Painter Durand
14 "Encore!"
15 La Scala solo
16 Impertinent
17 Po player in a casino game?
19 Carvel of 1492
20 Limited ___
21 "I Dood It" comedian
23 *Moll Flanders* author Defoe
24 *Earth in the Balance* subj.
25 Hispanic huzzahs
27 Contest forms
30 "FOR SALE," e.g.
33 Abided
35 Lose control
36 No-brainer card game
37 Bus. card address
38 Parched
39 "___ Around": Beach Boys
41 Face reddener
43 Highland girl
44 Foot jewelry
46 Gray-brown goose
48 Da ___, Vietnam
49 Sheepish reply?
53 Called on
56 Individuals
57 *Green Acres* cow
58 Floor a stand-up comedian?
60 "Be patient!"
61 "Chiquitita" band
62 Bay State motto word
63 White as a sheet
64 Lillian in *Birth of a Nation*
65 Active ingredient in Off!

DOWN

1 Assign journalists to military units
2 *A Woman Called ___* (1982)
3 Buckwheat, e.g.
4 Orange segment
5 Blandished
6 "Is it a hit ___ error?"
7 Barfly's two cents
8 Acorn droppers
9 Appearance
10 *H.M.S. Pinafore* extras
11 Stalk an *NCIS: Los Angeles* star?
12 "Outer" prefix
13 Reynolds in *Green Lantern*
18 Richard of *Jaws* fame
22 Clark of *Smallville*
26 Batted
27 "Bat Out of Hell" singer Foley
28 Trophy sides
29 1974 CIA-spoof movie
30 "Hot Lips" portrayer
31 Othello's lieutenant
32 Jealous *Rat Race* actor?
34 .0000001 joule
40 Apprentice
41 Cannes cherub
42 Wife of Isaac
43 Not able to run free
45 Resident doctor
47 "Popeye" Doyle, for one
50 Carried (by)
51 Absinthe flavor
52 Strong suit
53 *Home Again* host Bob
54 Cleopatra's maid
55 Mrs. Doubtfire's attire
56 Water pollutants
59 *Madama Butterfly* accessory

Sport Maze

Draw the shortest way from the ball to the goal. You can only move along vertical and horizontal lines, not along diagonal lines. The figure on each square indicates the number of squares the ball must be moved in the same direction. You can change direction at each stop.

1	4	5	5	4	4
2	4	4	2	4	2
4	1	3	2	4	4
1	4	2	3		5
1	2	1	4	3	3
3	4	3	5	4	3

change ONE

Change one letter in each of these two words to form a common two-word phrase.

GREED BINGERS

ONE LETTER LESS OR MORE

The word on the right side contains the letters of the word on the left side plus or minus the letter in the middle. One letter is already in the right place.

B E R M U D A S +T ☐ ☐ ☐ ☐ B ☐ ☐ ☐ ☐

WORD SEARCH Agriculture

All the words are hidden vertically, horizontally or diagonally—in both directions. The letters that remain unused form a sentence from left to right.

```
C A G A S P A R A G U S R I C
A U L M T U E R E P R O D U C
R E S A F B O O E L T T A C D
R I A N M T I U R F F S W E L
O L R U A S W O R C E R A C S
T O C R B R E E D I N G N T H
E U R E I G L H O O N W N D S
C S C S U G B C O H E O U L A
V S A U M F A C L R L D A I O
E W U R O E T T H R S A L A P
G B L P O S S Y I I S E F L I
E A I L R W T C R O C M A F N
T R F U H O F O Y E N O I U S
A L L S S C T R M T L L R D R
B E O E U A T C H A H E E Y A
L Y W E M R A N A D T E C B P
E S E M U G E L I R W O O F U
E Y R T L U O P P O T A T O L
```

- ANNUAL FAIR
- ASPARAGUS
- BARLEY
- BREEDING
- CARROT
- CATTLE
- CAULIFLOWER
- CELERY
- CHICORY
- COWS
- CUCUMBER
- FENNEL
- FLAIL
- FRUIT
- HORSE
- IRRIGATION
- LEGUMES
- MANURE SURPLUS
- MEADOW
- MUSHROOM
- PARSNIP
- POTATO
- POULTRY
- SCARECROW
- SCYTHE
- STABLE
- TOMATO
- TRACTOR
- VEGETABLE
- WEEDS

Last Name First

ACROSS

1 Ice-cream preference
5 *Caveman* star Ringo
10 Hole makers
14 *Bolero* instrument
15 "... and baby makes ___"
16 Flight of steps to a riverbank
17 Impressionist who needs a lift?
19 Adjutant
20 Beguiled
21 A time to dye
23 Apply spin
24 Parson's place
25 Arizona plant
28 Mardi Gras
31 Called for liniment
32 Retrogressing
33 Citrus cooler
34 *Abbey* ___ album
35 Barely burn
36 Fannie Mae: Abbrev.
37 "___ bodkins!"
38 Zellweger in *Bridget Jones's Diary*
39 Bamboo stems
40 Conferences
42 Supple
43 Ben in *Chariots of Fire*
44 Rapunzel's claim to fame
45 *Mutiny on the Bounty* island
47 Force upon again
51 Drummer Van Halen
52 Tan *Fringe* actress?
54 Tribe of Israel
55 *12 Angry Men* director
56 Starbuck's skipper
57 Stubby in "Cat Ballou"
58 "By jove!"
59 Big season at Toys "R" Us

DOWN

1 Keep back
2 Anne Nichols hero
3 Campus cadet org.
4 Abhorred
5 Allen and Martin
6 Chucked
7 Adjective for Death Valley
8 DVR button
9 Drill
10 1994 U.S. Open winner
11 Game show lady goes platinum blonde?
12 Do dock work
13 An end to fun?

18 Ariel Sharon's party
22 "Snowbird" singer Murray
24 One of the Simpsons
25 Rebound
26 Kipling's "___ of Morals"
27 Pursue a *Community* star?
28 Traffic markers
29 Blurb specialists
30 Rock-bottom
32 "Silly Love Songs" band
35 Displaying good judgment

36 What turnabout is
38 Street fight
39 "___ Ev'ry Mountain"
41 *Hi and Lois* baby
42 Spotted ponies
44 Chopped down
45 Blab
46 Epithet of Athena
47 Eternal City
48 *Hawaii Five-O* setting
49 Earth's crust
50 Kathryn of *Law & Order: CI*
53 Trapdoor cover

Keep Going

Start on a blank square of your choice and connect as many blank squares as possible with one single continuous line. You can only connect squares along vertical and horizontal lines, not along diagonal lines. You must continue the connecting line up until the next obstacle, i.e., the rim of the box, a black square or a square that has already been used. You can change direction at any obstacle you meet. Each square can only be used once. The number of blank squares that will be left unused is marked in the upper square. There is more than one solution. We only show one solution.

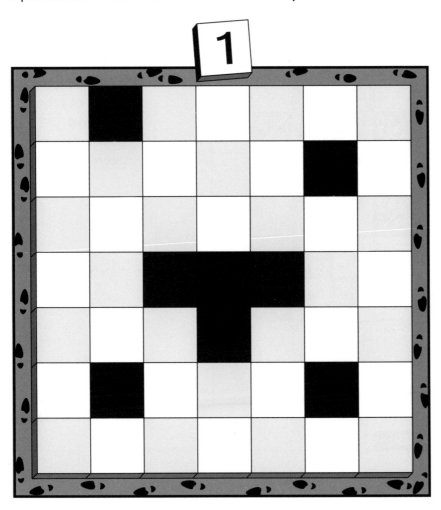

delete ONE

Delete one letter from
USE ARMS A LOT
and rearrange the rest to find a tumble?

Kakuro

Each number in a black area is the sum of the numbers that you have to enter in the next empty boxes. The empty boxes that make up the sum are called a run. The sum of the across run is written above the diagonal in the black area and the sum of the down run is written below the diagonal. Runs can only contain the numbers 1 through 9 and each number in a run can only be used once. The gray boxes only contain odd numbers and the white only even numbers.

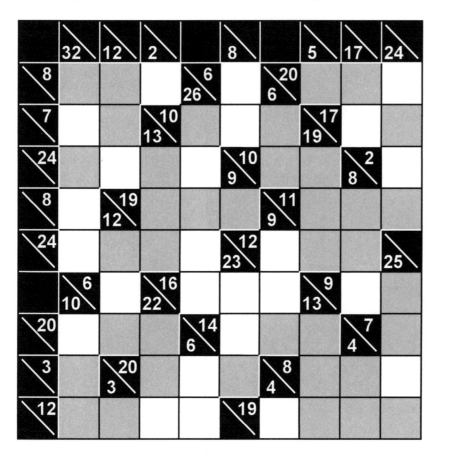

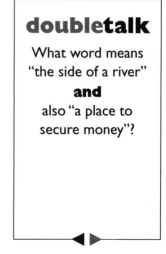

doubletalk

What word means "the side of a river" **and** also "a place to secure money"?

◄ ►

Fill in each missing letter, indicated by an X, to make a well-known proverb.

XX IS BXXXXR XX XIVX TXXN XECEXVE

Cage the Animals

Draw lines to completely divide up the grid into small squares with exactly one animal per square. The squares should not overlap.

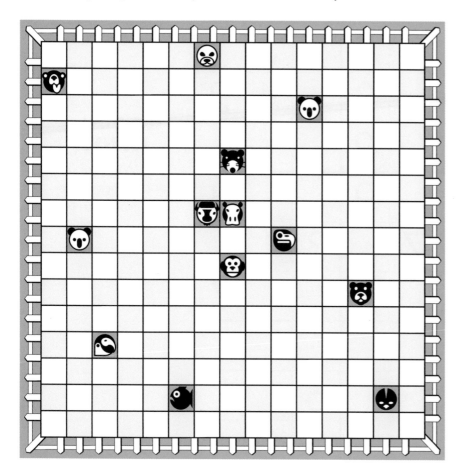

do you KNOW

What are the names of the six Gummi Bears?

_____

_____

LETTERBLOCKS

Move the letterblocks around so that words are formed on top and below that you can associate with countries.

Sudoku

Fill in the grid so that each row, each column and each 3 x 3 frame contains every number from 1 to 9.

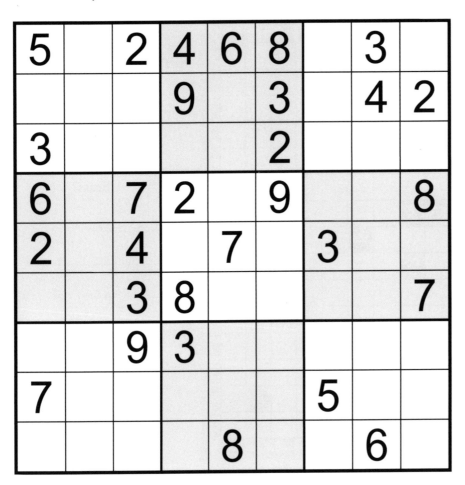

do you KNOW?

What are the names of the Three Wise Men?

_____

_____

FRIENDS

What do the following words have in common?

BASE GENETIC GRAM LOG METER PAUSE PHONE TRIBE

_____

CROSSWORD County Fair

ACROSS

1 Ferris ___, midway ride at the fair
6 Youth group at the fair (abbrev.)
9 Cinder
12 Word of greeting
13 Talk your ___ off
14 Shoshonean
15 In tune (2 words)
16 What we breathe
17 Sprinted
18 Building found at the fair (2 words)
21 John or Ringo
24 Guacamole alternative
25 Breakfast food
26 It goes with Dakota for Carolina
29 Female deer
30 It's north of Calif.
31 Health resort
34 Hebrew scroll
36 First Lady Truman
37 Once more
40 African tree
42 Prize given at the fair (2 words)
45 Set the ___ high
46 By ___ stretch of the imagination
47 City official
51 Time period
52 Actor from *The A-Team* (2 words)
53 Insipid
54 Affirmative
55 ___ eating contest at the fair
56 ___, fair snack favorite

DOWN

1 He ___ hesitates is lost
2 As protective as a mother ___
3 Yellowstone resident
4 Votes in
5 True-blue
6 Accomplishment
7 Antonym of succeed
8 Put handcuffs on
9 Pertaining to hearing
10 Distant suns
11 Type of tattoo
19 Male singing voice
20 ___ humbug!
21 Sleeping spot
22 Sense of self-worth
23 90 years, for example
27 Are you a man ___ mouse? (2 words)
28 Specialty of the Betty Ford Center
31 Less than a min.
32 Greek letter
33 Red ___ beet (2 words)
34 Make a knot
35 Highway entrance
36 Yellow fruit
37 Monastery
38 Look at angrily
39 Halos
41 Type of strip
43 Letters over Christ's head on the cross
44 Digital unit
48 Hairy beast
49 My ___ and only
50 Hi-___, describing a sharp image

Stack Tracking

Below you'll see a grid containing geometric shapes with the names of the shapes underneath. Your goal is to assure that the shapes and names match, so that each shape has a correct name in the corresponding position on the grid. If you run across a mistake, circle the incorrect word and continue on.

For example:

SQUARE   STAR   (STAR)   SQUARE

These exercises will be scored for accuracy. But time is also important, so work as quickly as possible. When you have completed each page, write down the amount of time you needed to finish in the space provided at the bottom. Score the exercise before moving on to the next one. Try to beat your time in subsequent exercises.

FOR THIS EXERCISE, YOU'LL NEED:
A pen or pencil • A stopwatch or watch or clock with a second hand

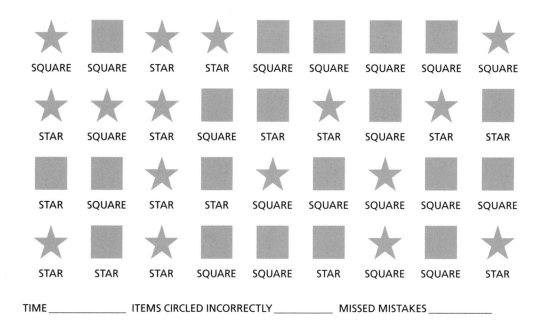

TIME _____ ITEMS CIRCLED INCORRECTLY _____ MISSED MISTAKES _____

SQUARE CHECK CIRCLE CIRCLE SQUARE CROSS SQUARE SQUARE SQUARE

STAR CIRCLE STAR CHECK STAR CROSS SQUARE STAR CROSS

STAR SQUARE STAR CIRCLE SQUARE SQUARE SQUARE SQUARE STAR

SQUARE CHECK CIRCLE CHECK STAR CROSS SQUARE SQUARE SQUARE

TIME _____ ITEMS CIRCLED INCORRECTLY _____ MISSED MISTAKES _____

FLOWER SQUARE STAR CROSS CHECK SQUARE SQUARE FLOWER SQUARE

STAR CIRCLE CIRCLE SQUARE STAR STAR FLOWER STAR CHECK

CROSS FLOWER STAR FLOWER CHECK SQUARE CIRCLE SQUARE SQUARE

CHECK FLOWER CIRCLE SQUARE STAR STAR FLOWER STAR CHECK

TIME _____ ITEMS CIRCLED INCORRECTLY _____ MISSED MISTAKES _____

CROSSWORD # Vintage Electronics

ACROSS

1 First born?
5 Pronto
9 Gives up
14 8, prefix
15 Type of tomato
16 Knock over
17 Its logo is Nipper the dog (2 words)
19 Yoga pose
20 Where to find Djibouti or Patagonia
21 Smooch
23 Inquire
24 Yoda, for one
27 Word before urchin or turtle
28 3rd letter
29 Electronics firm started in 1928
33 Unit of energy
35 A needle _____ haystack (2 words)
36 _____ *Gay* bomber
38 Most populous continent
42 Major organ
44 Dale, Roy's wife
46 Type of hockey shot
47 Org.
48 Sea eagles
50 Mature
51 Submachine gun
54 Vintage electronics firm formed in 1917
56 They replaced cassettes
59 List abbreviation
61 Den
62 Food scrap
63 High time?
65 Cable cars
69 The capital is Port-au-Prince
71 Began as Matsushita Electric in 1918
74 Ceremonial splendor

75 Nefarious
76 *Fixer Upper* setting
77 Nick
78 Farmer location?
79 Correct a correction

DOWN

1 TV chef Cat
2 CPA
3 Slanted letters (abbrev.)
4 Largest tribe in U.S.
5 St. Joan of _____
6 Drunkard
7 Run _____
8 Louvre locale
9 TV brand begun in '67
10 Shipping company

11 Scientist Newton
12 Anxious
13 Claim
18 French river
22 Homonym to 27 and 28 Across
25 Complete
26 _____ *Lucy* (2 words)
29 Actress Kunis
30 Burden
31 Sunbathes
32 Siren
34 Argon, for example
37 A year's record
39 Eastern European
40 Othello's enemy
41 High point
43 Wildebeest

45 Video game company
49 Hissy fits
52 Electronics company bought by LG
53 Famous '90s judge
55 Archery needs
56 Musician Leonard
57 Constellation
58 Wilt the _____ Chamberlain
60 Managed
64 Church area
66 Medical school subj.
67 Three Blind _____
68 Sean Connery, e.g.
70 Tic-_____-toe
72 Zilch
73 Total

WORD SEARCH In the Swim

All the words are hidden vertically, horizontally or diagonally—
in both directions.

```
W Z K T S C N L I A P O G D O F M T H
A I G A W F D Z W Y X S O J R P L Y T
T M O S I B Y I S Q P P M Z L U E B J
E T G J M W L X M O I C U L V H K D O
R N G L S J A A L A T X A H S D R V T
R Y L X U J A F N T D B S C G L O J L
K H E F I Y P P A K Y X O Z A S N M G
P M S K T I Z O C E E V L O R L S C V
C U G N L O L V L W E T B P E U C Y V
N A K F Q F T L G R L O S E M M B B W
A G L V T K O B U H O I J D A B B E B
X L S Y C V W P M K F I G G C R I A E
Z B S U N G L A S S E S A M Z E Y C E
A C J C F P D I P Q E Z H O S L X H B
B T D H A Q Y N K H I F F C N L Q B S
D A A A E O T C Y N I A J N N A M A I
O H X I X U N R E R Y X H B J U F G R
C P Q R A G I S K C O L B N U S L Q F
Y I X N I T O W E L R I C O O L E R L
```

- BEACH BAG
- BLANKET
- BOOK
- CAMERA
- CHAIR
- COOLER
- COVER UP
- FLIP FLOPS
- FLOAT
- FRISBEE
- GOGGLES
- HAT
- IPOD
- LUNCH
- MAGAZINES
- PAIL
- SNORKEL
- SUNBLOCK
- SUNGLASSES
- SWIMSUIT
- TOWEL
- UMBRELLA
- VOLLEYBALL
- WATER

Photography

All the words are hidden vertically, horizontally or diagonally—in both directions. The letters that remain unused form a sentence from left to right.

```
S L I D E P R O J E C T O R T
E U Q I N H C E T H M O D E L
E V M W E D A L B L E S S A H
P I E D N O M M R D P H O A T
I G G E L O E G O R A P H M Y
R N A V A T R I P O D I S A D
T E P E R E A O R I R V E R D
S T I L G F R L S R O K M O G
T T X O E T A U R E E K R N I
C I E P R T C X A L L A R A P
A N L A I O N A T U R E T P D
T G I G F L Z O O M L E N S I
N T I O T E R T H G I L A L L
O D T Y M E F A N X S W R S I
C U T S A T E L L I T E N I F
A P E R T U R E A F N E G I W
S H A R P N E S S S L I L T H
E V I T A G E N L I H M G H T
```

- APERTURE
- AUTOFOCUS
- CAMERA
- CONTACT STRIP
- DARKROOM
- DEVELOP
- DIGITAL
- ENLARGER
- FILM
- FIX
- FLASH
- HASSELBLAD
- LENS
- LIGHT
- MEGAPIXEL
- MODEL
- NATURE
- NEGATIVE
- PANORAMA
- PARALLAX
- PORTRAIT
- SATELLITE
- SHARPNESS
- SLIDE PROJECTOR
- TECHNIQUE
- TRIPOD
- VIGNETTING
- ZOOM LENS

TRIVIA QUIZ **Christmas Quiz**

It's the most musical time of the year.
How many of these holiday songs make your personal Yuletide soundtrack?

1. Written in 1942, it made the Billboard 100 every year until 1963.
   a. "I'll Be Home for Christmas"
   b. "Silver Bells"
   c. "White Christmas"

2. This 1944 song was deemed too sad until the singer helped to rewrite it.
   a. "Have Yourself a Merry Little Christmas"
   b. "(There's No Place Like) Home for the Holidays"
   c. "The Holly and the Ivy"

3. Cowritten by crooner Mel Torme, this was a hit for another beloved crooner.
   a. "Sleigh Ride"
   b. "Frosty the Snowman"
   c. "The Christmas Song"

4. This novelty hit in 1952 was by a 13-year-old singer.
   a. "I Want a Hippopotamus for Christmas"
   b. "I Saw Mommy Kissing Santa Claus"
   c. "Grandma Got Run Over by a Reindeer"

5. This jazzy 1953 hit was from the singer who later played Catwoman.
   a. "Here Comes Santa Claus"
   b. "Santa Baby"
   c. "Must Be Santa"

6. This is considered the first rock 'n' roll holiday hit.
   a. "Jingle Bell Rock"
   b. "Baby, It's Cold Outside"
   c. "Let It Snow"

7. It was on Elvis's first Christmas album in 1957.
   a. "Jingle Bells"
   b. "Winter Wonderland"
   c. "Blue Christmas"

8. It didn't chart until two years after Brenda Lee recorded it.
   a. "Santa Claus Is Coming to Town"
   b. "Rockin' Around the Christmas Tree"
   c. "Deck the Halls"

9. This one's a country favorite from Buck Owens.
   a. "Santa Claus Is Back in Town"
   b. "Thinking About Drinking for Christmas"
   c. "Santa Looked a Lot Like Daddy"

10. It appears in the popular stop-motion movie *Rudolph the Red-Nosed Reindeer*.
   a. "Holly Jolly Christmas"
   b. "The Wassail Song"
   c. "The First Noel"

Sudoku

Fill in the grid so that each row, each column and each 3 x 3 frame contains every number from 1 to 9.

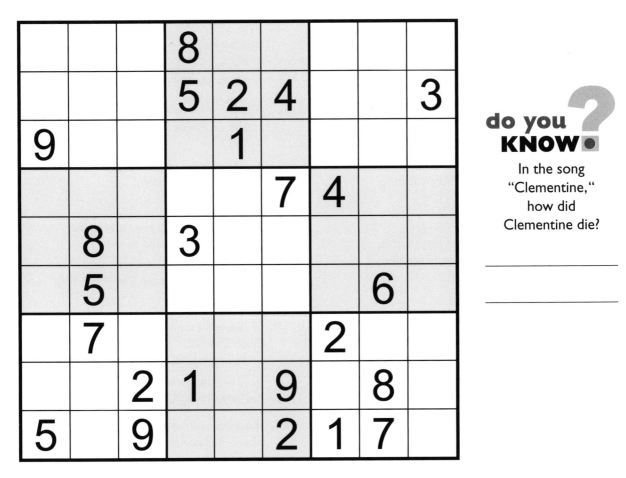

FRIENDS

What do the following words have in common?

ACT ATLANTIC CULTURAL FIGURE FIX FORM GENDER HIP

CROSSWORD Winter Warm-Ups

ACROSS

1 Angry Birds and Instagram, for example
5 Warm meal for a cold winter's night
9 ... and justice ___ all
12 A cat's defense
13 *Superman*, for example
14 "Don't mind ___ do" (2 words)
15 Charlotte Bronte's *Jane* ___
16 Warm headgear for winter
18 Slightly open
20 Bust in two
21 One who limits calories
24 In an evenhanded manner
25 Group of eight
26 Protrude
27 Erode
28 After safety or bobby
29 Unravel
33 Old dish towel
34 Make happy
35 Attack
39 *The ___ of Wrath*
40 Opposite of flat, in music
41 Fibrous food
42 Warm drink for a winter's day (2 words)
44 Space agency (abbrev.)
48 Antipollution agency (abbrev.)
49 Italian car company
50 Singer Church or Clapton
51 Important nine-digit number (abbrev.)
52 A ___ in the woodstove warms up a chilly winter night
53 Period of penitence and sometimes fasting

DOWN

1 Playing card with one pip
2 A layer, as of toilet paper
3 Average or norm
4 A warm pullover or cardigan ___ is cozy when it's cold
5 To remove fleece
6 Rip
7 Flub
8 Australian marsupial
9 One who plays a flutelike instrument
10 Waste parts
11 ___ *Business,* Tom Cruise movie
17 Psychic Geller
19 Airplane
21 ___ Jones Industrial Average
22 Cube for a drink
23 Airport stat (abbrev.)
24 Entertainment
26 Dance
28 Buddy
29 ___ pajamas or sheets add winter warmth
30 Knock sharply
31 Dined
32 Affirmative
33 Scam
34 Time period
35 *Angela's* ___
36 Stores
37 Lucifer
38 Circle segment
39 To shred cheese
41 Wild pig
43 102 in Roman numerals
45 When the chips ___ down
46 Transgression
47 Part of a play

WEATHER CHART Sunny

Where will the sun shine, if each arrow points in the direction of a spot where the symbol is located? The symbols cannot be next to each other vertically, horizontally or diagonally. A symbol cannot be placed on top of an arrow. We show one symbol.

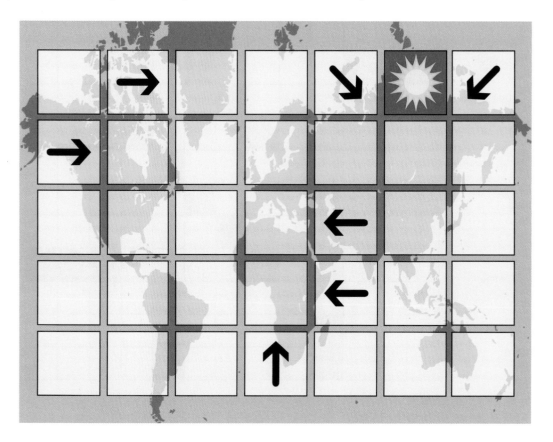

BLOCK ANAGRAM

Form the words that are described in the brackets with the letters above the grid. Extra letters are already in the right place.

LONESOME RIG (chamber)

Word Sudoku

Complete the grid so that each row, each column and each 3 x 3 frame contains the nine letters from the black box below. The hidden nine-letter word is in the diagonal from top left to bottom right.

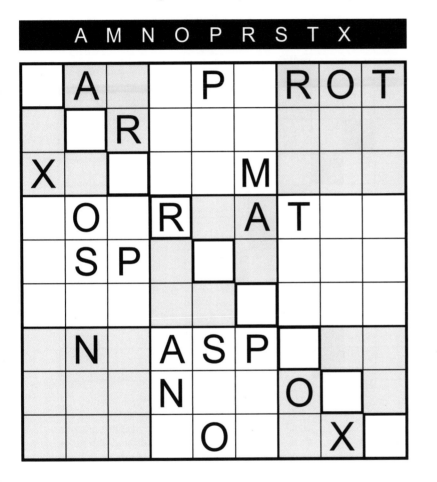

A M N O P R S T X

	A			P		R	O	T
		R						
X					M			
	O		R		A	T		
	S	P						
	N		A	S	P			
			N				O	
			O			X		

do you KNOW

What is a female donkey called?

_____

_____

An Old-Fashioned Christmas

ACROSS

1 Pole on a ship
5 Place for pampering
8 Celebrities (abbrev.)
12 Female singing voice
13 Barbie's boyfriend
14 Frozen drink brand name
15 Old-fashioned Christmas activity
17 Dry
18 Ginger ___
19 Wanted
21 Shiny old-fashioned Christmas tree decoration
24 Lion of constellation
25 Heart test (abbrev.)
26 Maneuver a boat
28 Blacksmith's need
32 Part of a woodwind instrument
34 "___ humbug!"
36 Lone
37 Super ___ video games
39 Bone protecting the lungs
41 Vietnam Veterans Memorial architect Maya
42 First aid technique (abbrev.)
44 See 8 Down
46 Singer Michael or Janet
50 *Glee* actress ___ Michele
51 Model ___ Macpherson
52 Old-fashioned Christmas tree decorations made of popcorn and cranberries
56 Color of a horse
57 Airport abbreviation
58 Word before finger
59 Used to open locks
60 Stage of sleep (abbrev.)
61 Leave hastily

DOWN

1 Apple computer
2 Pie ___ mode (2 words)
3 ___ than fiction
4 Hammer and wrench
5 Downhill or cross country
6 Await judgment or settlement
7 Christmas tree topper
8 "While ___ of sugarplums ___ in their heads," with 44 Across
9 One who frosts
10 Father (French)
11 Kernel
16 Ogle
20 Caspian, for one
21 Semester
22 Swedish home goods store
23 Easy throw
27 Kids' card game
29 Describing rock from Mount St. Helens
30 "Would ___ to you?" (2 words)
31 Loan
33 Charles ___ wrote *A Christmas Carol*
35 Concealed
38 Special ___ (elite Army units)
40 Word with basket or foot
43 Film critic Ebert
45 Gets close to
46 Move with a lurch
47 Soothing gel
48 Modeling substance
49 Designer Berkus
53 Male sheep
54 Genetic material
55 Army rank (abbrev.)

MIND MAZE # Know the Ropes

Have a close look at the ropes below. How many of these loops will form a knot if the rope is slowly pulled taut? (Where one rope passes under another, the bottom rope has been "cut away" slightly to aid visualization.)

Pop Music

All the words are hidden vertically, horizontally or diagonally—in both directions. The letters that remain unused form a sentence from left to right.

```
P O P M A G A G Y D A L G U S
K P I N C I N S N P A R R T O
F I E B A N A J E I U W C U L
T N N T O R V U A O T R A L P
O K C K I W R E B C R S C E P
T T L K S I I S O N K A F R T
O E A R I C N E E U Q S A T H
E H P W S I A A S H A D O W S
S R T S A D E R R I I N W N H
A I O G O T C H P O D Y L A N
N Y N C U L I T H E X U R E B
T E N E A G L E S P N E C A M
A S S E N D A M S E R T T T H
N E P U N D P B L T D I E T I
A C P R A O P P E O O R N R E
T B Y O H N A V O N O D F C S
E V B E I R Z R P O L I C E E
Y O N A R E S C O R P I O N S
```

- ABBA
- BOWIE
- CARPENTERS
- CLAPTON
- DONOVAN
- DOORS
- DYLAN
- EAGLES
- ENYA
- GAINSBOURG
- JACKSON
- KINKS
- LADY GAGA
- MADNESS
- NENA
- NIRVANA
- OASIS
- PINK
- POLICE
- PRINCE
- QUEEN
- RADIOHEAD
- RIHANNA
- ROXETTE
- SADE
- SANTANA
- SCORPIONS
- SHADOWS
- SHAKIRA
- STING
- TIESTO
- TOTO
- ZAPPA

Sudoku Twin

Fill in the grid so that each row, each column and each 3 x 3 frame contains every number from 1 to 9. A sudoku twin is two connected 9 x 9 sudokus.

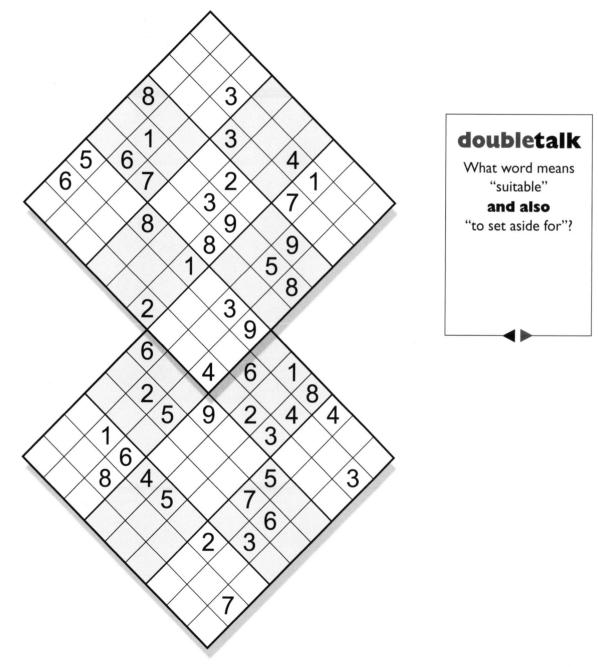

doubletalk

What word means
"suitable"
and also
"to set aside for"?

◀ ▶

Painter

Which paint (1–4) was used the most to color in the three shapes?

BLOCK ANAGRAM

Form the words that are described in the brackets with the letters above the grid.
Extra letters are already in the right place.

NORDIC ALP (major part of the central nervous system)

Binairo

Complete the grid with zeros and ones until there are 6 zeros and 6 ones in every row and every column. No more than two of the same number can be next to or under each other. Rows or columns with exactly the same content are not allowed. There is only one valid solution.

do you KNOW?

What does the Congo flow north and south of?

_____

_____

REPOSITION PREPOSITION

Unscramble **TIP IF NOON** and find a three-word preposition.

_____

Kakuro

Each number in a black area is the sum of the numbers that you have to enter in the next empty boxes. The empty boxes that make up the sum are called a run. The sum of the across run is written above the diagonal in the black area and the sum of the down run is written below the diagonal. Runs can only contain the numbers 1 through 9 and each number in a run can only be used once. The gray boxes only contain odd numbers and the white only even numbers.

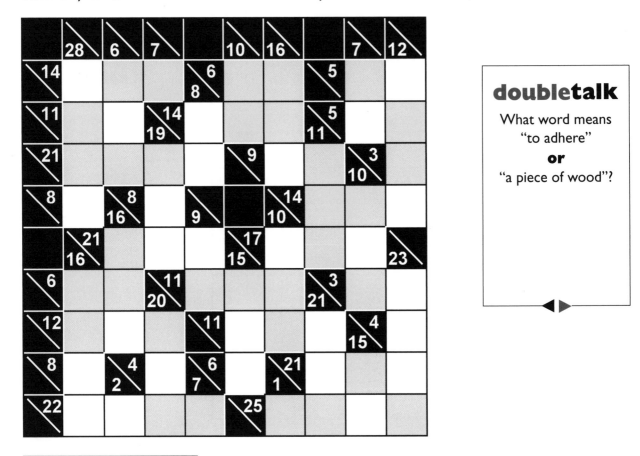

doubletalk

What word means
"to adhere"

or

"a piece of wood"?

CROSSWORD Wines

ACROSS

1 Borscht ingredient
5 Honey-colored
10 *Teacher's Pet* dog
14 Irish Gaelic
15 Witherspoon in *Water for Elephants*
16 Shroud
17 Masonry support
18 Kellogg's Pop-___
19 Novelist Bagnold
20 Flowery white wine
22 Leek relatives
24 Superlative Lake Tanganyika
25 With a good physique
26 Muesli morsel
27 Helena resident
30 Chief island of the Philippines
33 Nutritionist's topics
34 "Yang Yang" singer Yoko
35 PGA winner Dutra
36 Superhero wear
37 ___-Japanese War
38 Recyclable item
39 Opposite of hindered
40 Buckeye State city
41 In the know
43 LVII + XCIV
44 Nom de guerre
45 They'll curl your hair
49 Kindling
51 Sweet white wine
52 "Just You ___": Manchester
53 Newscast feature
55 FDR's dog
56 Home of Keebler elves
57 Egglike
58 School on the Rio Grande
59 Is under the weather
60 Of birth
61 Not so great

DOWN

1 Abe Lincoln grew one
2 Banks of baseball
3 Lauder of cosmetics
4 Cough syrup measure
5 Creative type
6 "And I said what I ___": Seuss
7 Composer of *Wozzeck*
8 Ottawa hrs.
9 Fills the air
10 Aussie girl
11 Full-bodied red wine
12 King of the Aesir
13 *Bill & ___ Excellent Adventure* (1989)
21 Rest against
23 Picky people pick 'em
25 Reacted to a bad call
27 Power bike
28 ___ Domini
29 Twelve sharp
30 Focal points
31 Polish lancer
32 Robust red wine
33 Grows ghostly
36 Oklahoma panhandle river
37 Virtuosic
39 Indy winner Luyendyk
40 Garfunkel's "___ Know"
42 Doo-wop selections
43 Coerce
45 *Giant* ranch
46 Put on cloud nine
47 Dramatis personae
48 Loses it
49 "See ya!"
50 Letters on the cross
51 Sing like Cleo Laine
54 Mendes in *Ghost Rider*

TRIVIA QUIZ **Motor Mania**

FOUR-WHEELED FUN!

1. What was the racing number of Herbie, the Love Bug?

   _____

2. . . . and which fruit do you associate with Herbie?

   _____

3. What breakthrough was made by a car called Thrust SSC in Nevada in 1997?

   _____

4. Which car manufacturer's name means "I Roll" in Latin?

   _____

5. Which car did James Bond drive in *Goldfinger*?

   _____

6. What car manufacturer acquired Bentley in 1931?

   _____

7. Which TV cops drove a red Ford Torino?

   _____

8. Which was the first car to sell a million?

   _____

9. What was the first name of the original Mr. Benz?

   _____

10. Which sports car featured in the movie *Back to the Future*?

    _____

11. What does the acronym NASCAR stand for?

    _____

12. What automobile is the longest-running and most-produced of a single design in history?
13. What Porsche model did James Dean die in?

    _____

14. What was the name and make of the car made famous by *The Dukes of Hazzard*?

    _____

15. What car did the first Batman drive?

    _____

16. What was Ford Mustang named after?

    _____

17. 75% of all cars produced by which manufacturer are still on the road?

    _____

Word Pyramid

Each word in the pyramid has the letters of the word above it, plus a new letter.

T
(1) point in time
(2) insect living in organized colonies
(3) volcano in Sicily
(4) broken
(5) feeding
(6) making hot
(7) instructing

do you KNOW●

Who is
Fred Flintstone's
wife?

_____

_____

T
1
2
3
4
5
6
7

Answers (Do You Know? and Trivia answers are on page 256)

PAGE 8
Baker's Bliss

W	H	I	S	K		A	B	S		S	T	P
A	A	R	O	N		R	O	E		P	E	A
D	R	A	M	A		R	O	L	L	I	N	G
		E	V	E			F	A	L	S	E	
P	R	E	H	E	A	T		I	D	L	E	S
A	E	R	O		S	A	T	E				
S	P	E	W		E	P	A		C	A	N	A
			C	L	A	M		O	S	H	A	
M	A	R	C	H		S	P	A	T	U	L	A
O	M	A	H	A		A	L	T				
V	A	N	I	L	L	A		L	A	P	S	E
E	N	D		K	I	N		E	G	G	O	N
R	A	Y		Y	E	N		Y	E	A	S	T

PAGE 9
Cage the Animals

LETTERBLOCKS • COTTON / LEATHER

PAGE 10
Keep Going

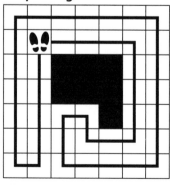

DELETE ONE • DELETE A AND FIND SPANISH SENORITA

PAGE 11
Winners

B	O	S	C		S	T	R	I	P		O	N	T	O
A	P	A	R		T	O	O	N	E		R	E	A	P
R	U	L	E	R	O	N	I	C	E		B	E	L	T
A	S	T	A	I	R	E		A	R	C	A	D	E	S
		M	G	M			L	A	C	Y				
D	E	S	P	I	S	E		M	E	T	H	O	D	S
E	L	C	I	D		D	R	O	S	S		U	R	E
A	C	H	E		V	E	I	N	S		G	N	A	W
L	A	W		G	E	N	O	A		B	R	O	K	E
T	R	A	D	E	R	S		S	C	R	E	W	E	D
	R	E	N	T			R	A	E					
C	A	T	T	A	I	L		F	I	F	T	I	E	S
H	A	Z	E		C	O	L	I	N	F	I	R	T	H
A	G	E	S		A	M	O	N	G		N	A	T	O
P	E	L	T		L	A	P	S	E		G	N	A	T

PAGE 12
Comfort Foods

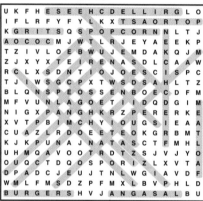

PAGE 13
Sport Maze

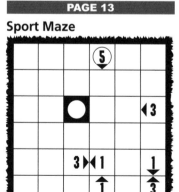

CHANGE ONE • BREAK DOWN

ONE LETTER LESS OR MORE • BANKERS

PAGE 14
Peanuts #1

H	E	M	P		S	T	O	O	P		E	W	E	R
O	B	O	E		V	A	L	V	E		R	O	T	O
F	E	R	N		E	L	I	A	S		R	O	T	A
F	R	A	N	K	L	I	N		T	R	A	D	E	R
A	T	L	A	N	T	A		M	E	E	T	S		
			N	E	E		V	E	R	B	A	T	I	M
G	E	S	T	E		K	O	R	E	A		O	R	I
O	R	C	S		B	U	I	L	D		I	C	A	L
O	S	H		M	E	R	C	E		A	S	K	E	D
P	E	R	S	U	A	D	E		O	R	O			
		O	A	S	T	S		P	R	A	L	I	N	E
F	E	E	D	E	R		R	E	D	B	A	R	O	N
R	E	D	D		I	S	E	R	E		T	O	L	D
O	R	E	L		C	H	E	L	A		E	N	T	E
M	O	R	E		E	A	S	E	L		D	Y	E	D

PAGE 15
Spot the Differences

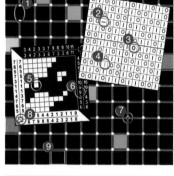

PAGE 16
Word Pyramid
E
(1) SE
(2) SET
(3) NEST
(4) INSET
(5) TENNIS
(6) INTENSE
(7) EINSTEIN

PAGE 17

Endless

A	S	T	O		A	B	F	A	B		C	A	M	E
B	E	A	V		L	I	E	T	O		A	G	A	R
L	A	K	E		T	O	T	A	L		T	O	R	S
E	T	E	R	N	A	L	T	R	I	A	N	G	L	E
		S	O	I				V	I	A				
A	L	G	E	B	R	A		T	I	M	P	A	N	I
H	I	R	E	E		S	A	R	A		I	A	N	
E	V	E	R	L	A	S	T	I	N	G	L	O	V	E
R	E	G		G	A	E	L		O	I	L	E	R	
O	N	G	U	A	R	D		L	E	F	T	I	S	T
		S	T	E			L	E	I					
F	O	R	E	V	E	R	Y	O	U	R	G	I	R	L
L	E	A	R		S	O	S	A	D		A	M	I	E
I	N	R	I		O	B	E	S	E		T	A	M	E
T	O	E	D		N	E	R	T	S		E	X	E	S

PAGE 18

Lost in Squares

PAGE 19

Sudoku

4	9	2	1	8	7	3	6	5
5	8	7	3	4	6	1	9	2
1	3	6	9	5	2	4	8	7
7	4	3	8	2	5	9	1	6
6	1	5	4	3	9	2	7	8
9	2	8	7	6	1	5	3	4
2	7	9	6	1	4	8	5	3
8	5	1	2	7	3	6	4	9
3	6	4	5	9	8	7	2	1

FRIENDS • EACH CAN HAVE THE PREFIX OUT- TO FORM A NEW WORD.

PAGE 20

Pet Dogs

B	R	O	M		A	S	C	O	T		E	S	P	Y
R	A	V	I		S	P	A	N	O		N	C	A	A
E	D	E	N		C	L	A	I	M		T	O	U	R
E	I	N	S	T	E	I	N		H	A	R	O	L	D
D	I	S	T	A	N	T		C	A	L	E	B		
		R	I	T		C	O	N	V	E	Y	E	D	
C	A	M	E	L		E	R	I	K	A		D	R	E
A	G	A	L		M	I	E	N	S		L	O	A	M
R	U	R		T	I	D	E	S		K	Y	O	T	O
R	E	M	A	I	N	E	D		H	E	R			
		A	D	L	E	R		S	E	N	I	O	R	S
L	A	D	D	E	R		S	P	R	O	C	K	E	T
E	L	U	L		A	L	A	R	M		I	A	M	A
N	I	K	E		L	I	K	E	A		S	P	A	R
S	E	E	D		S	T	E	E	N		T	I	N	T

PAGE 21

Balance the Scales

5 blue balls.
3 purple = 2 yellow + 2 blue (C = 2xA). 2 yellow = 2 blue + 2 purple (2xB). 3 purple = 4 blue + 2 purple. 1 purple = 4 blue. 1 yellow = 5 blue.

ONE LETTER LESS OR MORE • CATTAIL

PAGE 22

Binairo

I	O	I	O	I	O	O	I	I	O	I
O	I	O	I	I	O	I	O	I	I	O
I	I	O	I	O	I	O	I	O	I	O
I	O	I	O	I	O	I	I	O	O	I
O	O	I	I	O	I	I	O	I	O	I
I	I	O	O	I	I	O	O	I	I	O
O	O	I	I	O	O	I	I	O	I	I
I	I	O	I	O	I	I	O	I	O	O
O	I	I	O	I	O	O	I	I	O	I
I	O	O	I	O	I	I	O	O	I	I
O	I	I	O	I	I	O	I	O	I	O

REPOSITION PREPOSITION • EXCEPT FOR

PAGE 23

Did I Get That Right?

1. detritus (dih-'try-tuss)— [B] debris. People on our block are still picking up *detritus* from Billy's birthday bash.

2. prerogative (prih-'rah-guh-tiv)— [C] special right. If Dad wants to regift his dinosaur tie, that's his *prerogative.*

3. segue ('sehg-way)— [A] transition. But enough about you; let's *segue* to the topic of snakes.

4. hegemony (hih-'jeh-muh-nee)— [A] domination. Brian has complete *hegemony* over this Monopoly board.

5. dais ('day-iss)— [C] raised platform. The crowd threw tomatoes at the *dais* as the mayor began her press conference.

6. kefir (keh-'feer)— [B] fermented milk. Beth always eats the same breakfast: *kefir* mixed with nuts and fruit.

7. peremptory (puh-'remp-tuh-ree)— [A] allowing no disagreement. "I am not going to bed!" the toddler yelled in a *peremptory* tone.

8. quay (kee)— [A] wharf. Passengers waiting on the *quay* prepared to board the ferry.

9. machination (ma-kuh-'nay-shun)— [C] scheme. Despite all his *machinations,* Wile E. Coyote can't catch Road Runner.

10. slough (sloo)— [C] swamp. The *slough* is home to a variety of species, including salmon, ducks, and otters.

11. spurious ('spyuhr-ee-us)— [B] fake. So that UFO sighting in Central Park turned out to be *spurious?*

12. nuptial ('nuhp-shuhl)— [B] relating to marriage. I've attached a string of tin cans to the *nuptial* sedan.

13. coxswain ('kahk-suhn)— [C] sailor in charge. It's traditional for a winning crew to toss its *coxswain* overboard.

14. geoduck ('goo-ee-duhk)— [C] large Pacific clam. A *geoduck* can weigh over ten pounds—and live for more than 150 years!

15. plethora ('pleh-thuh-ruh)— [B] abundance. Joe claims a *plethora* of proof that Bigfoot exists.

VOCABULARY RATINGS

9 and below: mumbling
10–12: well-spoken
13–15: eloquent

Answers

Draw the Line

END GAME •
(C O E X T E N D)
(S P L E N D I D)
(E N D U R I N G)
(L A V E N D E R)

St. Patrick's Day

J	A	M	B		R	A	N	T		A	V	A
O	P	A	L		E	C	R	U		B	I	N
Y	O	G	A		S	H	A	M	R	O	C	K
		R	A	T	E		B	E	V	E	L	
F	I	E	N	D	S		C	L	E	E	S	E
I	M	B	E	D		M	A	E				
B	A	B	Y		P	O	T		E	L	B	A
		M	I	D		S	M	E	A	R		
P	O	E	T	I	C		T	E	E	T	H	E
A	R	M	O	R		S	O	A	R			
L	I	M	E	R	I	C	K		A	R	E	A
M	O	A		O	K	A	Y		L	O	N	G
A	N	S		R	E	N	O		D	O	D	O

Sunny

BLOCK ANAGRAM •
STEWARDESS

Word Sudoku

TRANSADDITION • ADD I AND T
AND FIND CONTRADICTION

NYC

M	O	L	L		P	E	T	A	L		A	D	A	M
A	G	I	O		O	V	E	R	A		N	O	L	A
R	E	N	I		P	E	R	E	C		S	T	A	R
C	E	N	T	R	A	L	P	A	R	K	W	E	S	T
			E	A	R			O	I	E				
T	H	E	R	I	T	Z		T	S	T	R	A	P	S
H	A	G	E	N		A	M	A	S			G	I	A
A	V	E	R	Y	F	I	S	H	E	R	H	A	L	L
N	E	S			A	R	G	O		E	A	M	E	S
E	S	T	E	L	L	E		E	S	T	R	A	D	A
			S	O	S			H	A	D				
S	T	A	T	U	E	O	F	L	I	B	E	R	T	Y
L	O	B	E		T	A	L	O	N		N	O	H	O
A	L	O	E		T	H	I	N	E		E	B	A	Y
P	L	U	M		O	U	T	E	R		D	O	D	O

Cage the Animals

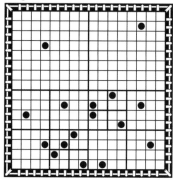

LETTERBLOCKS •
DESPAIR / PASSION

Keep Going

DELETE ONE • DELETE S AND FIND
CONFESSIONAL

Sleuths

S	C	O	P		S	H	A	R	P		S	L	A	W
I	R	A	E		P	O	L	A	R		L	E	D	A
M	I	S	S	M	A	R	P	L	E		O	W	E	N
B	E	T	T	E	R	S		E	L	E	G	A	N	T
A	S	S	E	T	S			A	D	A	R			
			R	E	E	K		S	T	E	N	C	I	L
T	O	N	E	R		R	I	P	E	N		H	O	E
A	P	E	D		H	E	R	E	S		S	E	N	T
L	A	R		I	O	W	A	N		M	A	R	A	T
C	H	O	R	T	L	E		D	I	A	L			
			W	A	S	I			S	H	E	R	P	A
A	V	O	C	A	D	O		F	L	A	S	H	E	S
D	A	L	I		A	D	R	I	A	N	M	O	N	K
A	L	F	A		Y	E	A	R	N			A	N	N	E
H	E	E	L		S	A	T	E	D		N	E	E	D

Trivial Pursuit 1952

1. *American Bandstand*
2. *The Adventures of Ozzie & Harriet*
3. *I've Got a Secret*
4. *Adventures of Superman*
5. *The Jackie Gleason Show*
6. *Our Miss Brooks*

TEST YOUR RECALL •
KELLOGG'S FROSTED FLAKES

PAGE 33

Sudoku

4	3	1	5	2	9	8	6	7
2	7	6	3	8	4	1	5	9
5	8	9	1	6	7	4	2	3
6	4	2	9	5	1	7	3	8
9	5	7	6	3	8	2	4	1
3	1	8	4	7	2	5	9	6
7	2	3	8	4	6	9	1	5
1	6	4	7	9	5	3	8	2
8	9	5	2	1	3	6	7	4

PAGE 34

City Nicknames

H	E	M	I		O	P	E	R	A		A	M	E	N
I	R	A	N		K	A	R	E	N		L	I	L	A
K	A	N	S	A	S	C	I	T	Y		M	L	I	I
E	S	T	I	M	A	T	E		T	R	O	W	E	L
S	E	A	S	O	N	S		L	H	A	S	A		
		T	S	A		M	O	I	S	T	U	R	E	
T	I	B	E	T		B	O	O	N	E		K	E	A
R	O	A	D		P	R	O	N	G		D	E	N	S
A	W	L		T	E	A	R	S		S	E	E	D	Y
P	A	T	I	E	N	C	E		P	E	A			
	I	R	E	N	E		G	O	O	D	B	Y	E	
P	O	M	O	N	A		T	R	O	U	B	L	E	D
A	V	O	N		N	E	W	O	R	L	E	A	N	S
B	A	R	I		T	R	I	P	E		A	R	T	E
A	L	E	C		S	A	N	E	R		T	E	A	L

PAGE 35

All Square

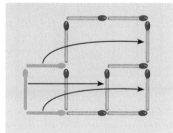

DOODLE PUZZLE • COME BACK

PAGE 36

Sport Maze

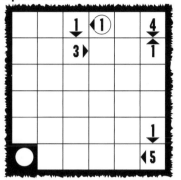

CHANGE ONE • RUSH HOUR

ONE LETTER LESS OR MORE • AFFLICT

PAGE 37

Pet Cats

O	L	A	F		C	U	B	I	C		S	T	E	T
S	O	H	O		A	R	E	N	A		T	H	I	S
A	G	A	R		M	A	N	O	F		O	O	N	A
G	A	R	F	I	E	L	D		F	A	R	M	E	R
E	N	D	E	A	R	S		S	E	L	M	A		
			I	N	A		T	H	I	E	S	S	E	N
M	I	S	T	S		S	E	I	N	E		I	L	A
R	O	Y	S		B	L	A	R	E		S	N	A	P
E	L	L		A	L	E	R	T		S	C	A	L	E
D	E	V	E	L	O	P	S		A	L	A			
		E	X	I	S	T		S	T	A	B	L	E	S
T	A	S	T	E	S		S	N	O	W	B	A	L	L
E	N	T	E		O	F	T	E	N		A	T	E	E
A	T	E	N		M	E	L	E	E		R	E	N	E
M	A	R	T		S	W	O	R	D		D	R	A	T

PAGE 38

Match Maker

BLOCK ANAGRAM • BARACK OBAMA

PAGE 39

Wedding Bells

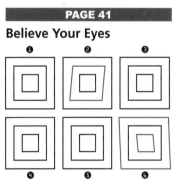

PAGE 40

April Showers

B	R	E	A	D		A	H	A		S	I	R
A	T	A	R	I		C	O	P		M	O	O
T	E	R	R	A		M	O	R	N	I	N	G
		I	N	R	E	D		A	L	I	E	
I	L	O	V	E	A		I	H	E	A	R	
N	O	P	E		D	O	W	N				
C	U	T		L	I	A	R	S		J	A	W
			M	O	R	E		S	O	L	O	
C	A	B	I	N		S	I	N	G	I	N	
A	L	A	N		N	O	T	R	E			
R	A	I	N	B	O	W		A	E	R	I	E
E	M	T		U	S	E		T	R	A	C	K
S	O	S		R	E	D		E	S	T	E	E

PAGE 41

Believe Your Eyes

Only groups 2 and 6

BLOCK ANAGRAM • SALMONELLA

Answers

PAGE 42

Insulation

1223. The order of the layers is identical to the first layer of insulation. The 5 colors rotate from right to left 1223, 2334, 3445, 4551, 5112, 1223, etc.

DOODLE PUZZLE • CLOCKWISE

PAGE 43

Binairo

0	1	1	0	0	1	1	0	1	0	1	0
1	0	1	0	1	0	0	1	0	1	0	1
0	1	0	1	0	1	1	0	0	1	0	1
0	0	1	0	1	1	0	1	1	0	1	0
1	1	0	1	0	0	1	0	1	0	0	1
1	0	0	1	0	0	1	1	0	1	1	0
0	1	1	0	1	1	0	0	1	0	1	0
1	0	0	1	1	0	1	0	0	1	0	1
0	0	1	0	0	1	0	1	1	0	1	1
1	1	0	0	1	0	0	1	1	0	1	0
1	0	1	1	0	1	1	0	0	1	0	0
0	1	0	1	1	0	0	1	0	1	0	1

REPOSITION PREPOSITION • IN ADDITION TO

PAGE 44

War

1. **a.** War of 1812
2. **b.** Disease
3. **a.** Kansas
4. **c.** Britain
5. **b.** Civil War
6. **c.** 19th
7. **c.** Gerald Ford
8. **d.** Kuwait
9. **c.** Both
10. **a.** Battle of Gettysburg

PAGE 45

Best-Sellers #1

PAGE 46

Meet the Parents

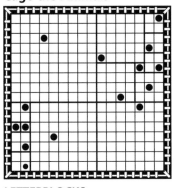

PAGE 47

Cage the Animals

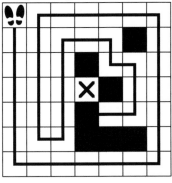

**LETTERBLOCKS •
BIOLOGY / TEACHER**

PAGE 48

Circle Grams

1. quality
2. realize
3. deserve
4. pianist
5. cheeses
6. theater
7. hopeful
8. ominous
9. abdomen

PAGE 49

Wall Street Symbolism

PAGE 50

Keep Going

**DELETE ONE •
DELETE S AND FIND UNSEAWORTHY**

PAGE 51

Rocket

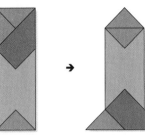

LETTER LINE • PARATROOPS;
PASTA, PARROT, ROTOR, SOAP, SPOOR

PAGE 52

Olympic Host Cities

A	R	F	S		B	O	A	R	D		A	B	B	A
L	E	A	P		A	L	B	E	E		N	A	A	N
L	A	K	E	P	L	A	C	I	D		G	R	I	T
I	C	I	C	L	E	S		D	I	R	E	C	T	S
S	T	R	I	A	E			C	O	L	E			
		M	I	N	T		S	A	V	A	L	A	S	
L	O	V	E	D		O	V	A	T	E		O	D	A
I	M	A	N		A	B	A	T	E		A	N	O	N
E	E	N		O	B	E	L	I		I	M	A	G	E
U	N	C	A	N	N	Y		E	S	T	E			
		O	L	E	O			M	A	R	C	U	S	
R	H	U	B	A	R	B		V	A	L	I	A	N	T
E	A	V	E		M	E	X	I	C	O	C	I	T	Y
A	V	E	R		A	L	E	C	K		A	R	I	L
P	E	R	T		L	A	D	E	S		S	N	E	E

PAGE 53

Word Sudoku

C	N	H	M	O	E	A	R	Z
O	A	R	Z	C	N	H	E	M
Z	E	M	R	A	H	N	O	C
H	M	C	E	Z	O	R	N	A
N	O	A	H	R	C	Z	M	E
R	Z	E	N	M	A	C	H	O
E	C	O	A	N	R	M	Z	H
M	H	N	C	E	Z	O	A	R
A	R	Z	O	H	M	E	C	N

UNCANNY TURN •
TWELVE PLUS ONE

PAGE 54

Spot the Differences

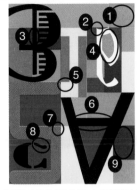

BLOCK ANAGRAM • AUSTRALIA

PAGE 55

Arbor Day

P	E	C	A	N		C	A	R		F	L	A
E	L	O	P	E		O	D	E		R	O	D
P	I	P	P	A		D	O	G	W	O	O	D
			A	T	E		R	I	N	S	E	
H	E	M	L	O	C	K		E	N	T	E	R
O	V	A	L		O	N	I	T				
G	E	T	S		L	E	G		A	N	E	W
			K	E	E	L		L	I	R	A	
O	B	A	M	A		D	O	U	G	L	A	S
S	O	L	A	R		O	N	E				
C	Y	P	R	E	S	S		A	R	E	T	E
A	L	E		E	E	L		R	I	S	E	S
R	E	N		M	A	Y		M	A	P	L	E

PAGE 56

Sudoku Twin

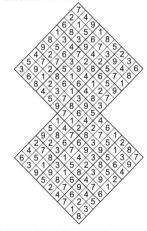

DOUBLETALK • RESIGN

PAGE 57

Sport Maze

CHANGE ONE • BAD BLOOD

ONE LETTER LESS OR MORE •
INHALER

PAGE 58

Catching Some Zs

S	H	A	G		T	E	P	E	E		A	B	I	T
O	O	N	A		E	L	I	Z	A		V	E	D	A
F	U	Z	Z	B	U	S	T	E	R		O	D	O	R
T	R	I	E	S	T	E		R	A	S	C	A	L	S
G	I	O	T	T	O			C	H	E	Z			
			T	A	N	A		C	H	U	T	Z	P	A
D	E	F	E	R		G	R	U	E	L		L	E	N
I	B	I	S		T	I	N	T	S		B	E	A	N
R	O	Z		G	H	O	S	T		P	A	D	R	E
E	N	Z	Y	M	E	S		Y	O	L	K			
		L	E	E	R			C	A	L	I	P	H	
E	L	E	A	N	O	R		C	E	T	A	C	E	A
M	E	O	R		P	I	Z	Z	A	O	V	E	N	S
M	A	U	L		E	V	I	A	N		A	U	N	T
A	R	T	Y		S	E	A	R	S		S	P	E	E

PAGE 59

Sudoku

8	4	7	9	3	1	6	2	5
1	3	5	8	6	2	7	9	4
9	6	2	4	7	5	1	3	8
6	5	9	7	2	4	3	8	1
4	7	3	1	8	9	5	6	2
2	1	8	3	5	6	9	4	7
5	8	1	2	9	3	4	7	6
3	2	6	5	4	7	8	1	9
7	9	4	6	1	8	2	5	3

Be Mine

```
V M E O P T C W C D G L R D Y U N S C
S S G O D N E I K M F H A I G R X N O
F P A S S I O N N I A T U S T R A E H
X S B L Z G H S P P E T S G Z O D Z H
S A O S W Y W Z R G V J E U S H Y U Q
W V Q U C Q N C K A A P S A S J O A C
E F B Z H Z V W L Z A D O R L M E E R
E P U V E M S E Q V R D R O A O A B J
T I Y R G S N E C E J P N J C H D J I
H Y O H I T C V A N V F Q B E Z I M D
E D L K I E G O R U U D L Q O K P I G
A F T N H T G A D S Y E Q O T I U N T
R O E F Y A L R D G H A J E W T C D I
T E E R X L Q L S T M A F R I E N D E
X D R F R O T H C A N D Y I O N R D I
A R Z X P C P S A X M S B X A L L S E
W N U Z D O C T K D R E N N I D B R S
R T A P E H V M N Z P G Y B P P R J T
L N E K R C X B E D A N E R E S P P U
```

I'll Have a Cold One

1. One liter
2. Cherries
3. It's roasted
4. India (India Pale Ale)
5. Lambic
6. The Czechs, followed by the Irish and the Germans
7. Not chilling beer reveals a wider range of flavors
8. The yeast used in brewing

TEST YOUR RECALL •
1-G, 2-C, 3-E, 4-I, 5-B, 6-A, 7-H, 8-F, 9-D

Body Language

1. mental—[B] of or relating to the chin. The boxing vet gave the cocky kid a little *mental* reminder halfway through the first round.

2. visage—[A] face. Harlan stared hard at the *visage* in the painting, curious about its smile.

3. hirsute—[C] hairy. "That's a great costume," Alan admitted. "But you're missing the *hirsute* hobbit feet."

4. pectoral—[C] of the chest. The weight lifter flexed his *pectoral* muscles in a truly Hulkian spectacle.

5. corpulent—[B] bulky or stout. Tara wouldn't call her brother overweight, just a little *corpulent*.

6. alopecia—[B] baldness. Art has been shaving his head since he was 21, hoping to hide his *alopecia*.

7. nuque—[A] back of the neck. Grazing Mary's *nuque*, Hugo thought, was a subtle sign of affection. She disagreed.

8. hemic—[B] of the blood. Would it be fair to say the *Twilight* characters have a slight *hemic* obsession?

9. gangling—[C] awkwardly tall and thin. The new teacher was a *gangling* figure from Sleepy Hollow, best known for another spindly pedagogue, Ichabod Crane.

10. cerumen—[C] earwax. "I certainly doubt *cerumen* is keeping you from hearing me," the instructor barked, glaring at her student's headphones.

11. pollex—[B] thumb. "That's a thimble," Gracie explained to her granddaughter during their sewing lesson. "It's the best way to protect your *pollex*."

12. ventral—[A] around the stomach. His *ventral* fat, the *Biggest Loser* contestant hoped, would be the first to go.

13. axilla—[C] armpit. The second grader's favorite gag involved his cupped hand and his *axilla*.

14. ossicles—[A] small bones in the ear. "For extra credit, what are the smallest bones in the human body?" Mr. Griffin asked. "The *ossicles*!" Tad shouted out.

15. fontanel—[C] soft spot in a young skull. "Mind his *fontanel*," the new mom said, handing her son to his nervous father.

VOCABULARY RATINGS
9 and below: thickheaded
10–12: clearheaded
13–15: eggheaded

Upbeat

M	E	E	K		A	S	P	I	C		G	H	I	A

Color It

Paint 2. Enough paint was used from 1 and 3 to color in a full square.

LETTER LINE • EVACUATION; NOVICE, ACUTE, TUNA, CAVE

Sudoku X

8	6	5	9	1	4	2	3	7
2	9	7	8	5	3	1	6	4
3	4	1	2	7	6	9	8	5
5	3	9	4	6	8	7	1	2
4	8	6	1	2	7	5	9	3
7	1	2	3	9	5	6	4	8
6	2	4	7	8	1	3	5	9
9	5	3	6	4	2	8	7	1
1	7	8	5	3	9	4	2	6

SANDWICH • IRON

PAGE 66

State Flags #1

J	O	G	S		S	T	E	M	S		S	T	E	P
A	R	O	W		P	E	E	V	E		P	E	R	U
C	A	L	I	F	O	R	N	I	A		U	N	I	T
O	L	D	G	L	O	R	Y		H	O	R	N	E	T
B	E	A		A	N	Y		F	O	S	S	E		
			O	P	S		S	O	R	E		S	O	S
M	E	L	D	S		C	U	R	S	E		S	L	O
A	R	O	D		M	I	N	C	E		L	E	A	F
S	T	U		R	E	V	U	E		S	I	E	N	A
S	E	I		B	L	I	P		M	T	V			
	S	K	I	L	L		M	A	E		U	V	A	
A	R	I	O	S	O		T	E	R	R	A	P	I	N
B	O	A	T		W	A	S	H	I	N	G	T	O	N
B	A	N	C		E	L	A	T	E		R	O	L	E
A	M	A	H		D	O	R	A	L		A	N	A	S

PAGE 67

Keep Going

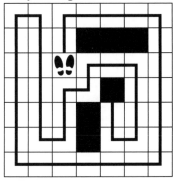

DELETE ONE • DELETE D AND FIND AN EXOTIC ICE TRIP

PAGE 68

Cage the Animals

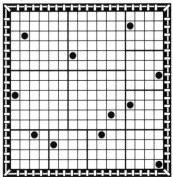

LETTERBLOCKS • BLOCKS /PUZZLES

PAGE 69

Earth Day

B	I	N	G		P	I	C	K		G	A	S
A	P	E	R		O	L	I	O		U	S	A
T	O	T	O		P	L	A	S	T	I	C	S
			C	A	P	S		H	E	L	O	S
O	R	N	E	R	Y		B	E	A	T	T	Y
H	E	A	R	T		W	A	R				
M	O	B	Y		H	A	D		R	A	R	E
			S	I	X		P	E	R	I	L	
C	H	I	R	P	S		G	E	C	K	O	S
L	O	N	E	R		P	I	T	Y			
A	L	U	M	I	N	U	M		C	H	A	D
P	E	S		N	O	R	M		L	O	V	E
S	S	E		T	R	E	E		E	W	E	S

PAGE 70

Bee's-Eye View

There are five occurrences of the pattern.

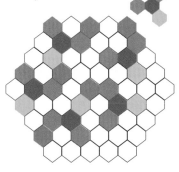

PAGE 71

Binairo

1	0	0	1	1	0	0	1	1	0	1
1	1	0	1	0	0	1	0	1	1	0
0	1	1	0	1	1	0	1	0	1	0
1	0	1	1	0	0	1	1	0	0	1
0	1	0	1	0	1	1	0	1	1	0
0	0	1	0	1	1	0	1	1	0	1
1	1	0	1	1	0	1	0	0	1	0
0	1	1	0	0	1	1	0	1	0	1
1	0	1	0	1	1	0	1	0	1	0
1	0	0	1	0	0	1	1	0	1	1
0	1	1	0	1	1	0	0	1	0	1

REPOSITION PREPOSITION • ON BEHALF OF

PAGE 72

Low Points

S	T	A	G		F	O	L	I	C		E	L	A	N
L	I	D	A		A	L	U	L	A		L	U	K	E
O	A	H	U		U	L	N	A	R		I	L	I	A
G	R	A	N	D	C	A	N	Y	O	N	J	U	M	P
S	A	N	T	E	E			L	E	A				
			L	P	T	S		B	I	G	H	O	R	N
I	S	L	E	T		T	E	E	N		L	A	E	
D	E	A	T	H	V	A	L	L	E	Y	D	A	Y	S
E	M	I		A	R	A	L		E	A	V	E	S	
S	E	R	P	E	N	T		O	R	A	N			
			A	N	I		U	R	S	U	L	A		
V	A	L	L	E	S	M	A	R	I	N	E	R	I	S
E	V	I	L		H	A	G	E	N		U	G	L	I
S	O	L	E		E	L	A	T	E		S	E	L	A
T	W	I	T		D	A	R	E	D		E	D	E	N

PAGE 73

Sudoku

5	7	8	3	2	1	6	4	9
3	9	6	4	8	7	2	1	5
2	4	1	9	5	6	8	7	3
9	5	2	7	3	4	1	8	6
8	6	3	5	1	2	7	9	4
7	1	4	8	6	9	3	5	2
6	8	5	1	9	3	4	2	7
4	3	9	2	7	8	5	6	1
1	2	7	6	4	5	9	3	8

FRIENDS • EACH CAN HAVE THE PREFIX BE- TO FORM A NEW WORD.

PAGE 74

Chill Out

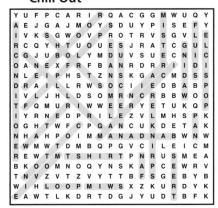

Answers

PAGE 75

Power Panels

33.50. An undamaged solar panel generates an amount of energy that is equal to the number of small complete squares in the grid. There are 34 squares in total: 32 complete and 4 half squares.

DOODLE PUZZLE • RE**PAIR**

PAGE 76

Word Sudoku

E	U	G	M	I	S	A	T	Z
A	S	M	T	Z	E	G	I	U
Z	I	T	G	A	U	M	S	E
S	E	A	I	T	G	Z	U	M
I	G	U	E	M	Z	S	A	T
M	T	Z	S	U	A	E	G	I
G	M	S	U	E	I	T	Z	A
T	Z	I	A	S	M	U	E	G
U	A	E	Z	G	T	I	M	S

TRANSADDITION •
ADD A AND FIND NATURALIST

PAGE 77

High Points

S	A	L	S		S	H	E	L	F		T	H	A	W
H	A	E	C		H	E	R	E	I		R	O	S	E
A	R	T	E		A	R	I	A	L		A	L	T	A
M	O	U	N	T	W	A	S	H	I	N	G	T	O	N
U	N	S	E	A	L			P	O	I				
		O	R	S	K		P	I	N	C	H	E	D	
S	T	I	N	T		E	D	E	N		A	A	A	
P	I	K	E	S	P	E	A	K	O	R	B	U	S	T
A	D	E		E	N	N	E		O	U	T	T	A	
M	E	A	S	U	R	E		S	P	A	S			
		A	H	S			S	C	R	A	P	E		
H	E	A	D	F	O	R	T	H	E	H	I	L	L	S
E	N	I	D		N	O	Y	O	U		D	E	A	N
L	O	D	E		A	S	E	E	D		E	V	I	E
P	L	A	N		L	A	S	S	O		S	E	T	S

PAGE 78

Best in Show

PAGE 79

Sport Maze

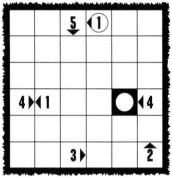

CHANGE ONE • SEA CHANGE

ONE LETTER LESS OR MORE •
CHAPERONE

PAGE 80

Binairo

I	I	O	O	I	O	I	O	O	I	I
O	I	I	O	I	I	O	I	I	O	O
I	O	O	I	O	I	I	O	I	I	O
O	O	I	I	O	O	I	I	O	I	I
I	I	O	O	I	I	O	I	I	O	O
I	O	I	I	O	I	I	O	I	O	O
O	I	O	I	I	O	I	O	O	I	I
I	O	I	O	I	I	O	I	O	O	I
I	I	O	I	O	O	I	O	I	I	O
O	O	I	I	O	I	O	I	I	O	I
O	I	I	O	I	O	O	I	O	I	I

REPOSITION PREPOSITION •
OWING TO

PAGE 81

Way Out

Point E. At every intersection the driver chooses the shortest way to the next intersection.

BLOCK ANAGRAM •
SCHOOLTEACHER

PAGE 82

Sunny

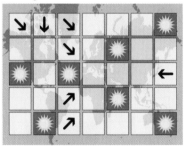

BLOCK ANAGRAM • FOOTBALL PLAYER

PAGE 83

Rosie the Riveter

1. 44 percent
2. *The Saturday Evening Post*
3. She has a halo floating just above her visor
4. 27 percent
5. Richmond, California
6. Kaiser Permanente
7. A housing complex built for the shipyard workers
8. Norman Rockwell's

TEST YOUR RECALL •
1. Marlboro
2. Chesterfield 101s
3. Virginia Slims
4. Tareyton
5. Winston
6. Kent
7. Camel

PAGE 84

Sudoku

8	5	7	6	1	3	4	2	9
1	4	6	9	2	5	3	7	8
9	3	2	4	7	8	1	6	5
4	1	9	2	5	7	8	3	6
7	8	5	3	6	4	9	1	2
2	6	3	1	8	9	7	5	4
5	9	1	8	3	2	6	4	7
6	2	4	7	9	1	5	8	3
3	7	8	5	4	6	2	9	1

FRIENDS • EACH CAN HAVE THE
PREFIX SUB- TO FORM A NEW WORD.

PAGE 85

Skewered

0.30. Six meatballs cost 6 x 2 = 12
sausages. 9 beef cubes cost 9 x 2 =
18 meatballs x 2 = 36 sausages. You
pay a total of 16.20 for 12 + 36 + 6
= 54 sausages or 16.20/54 = 0.30 per
sausage.

DOODLE PUZZLE • RED**UCE**

PAGE 86

Peanuts #2

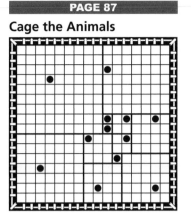

PAGE 87

Cage the Animals

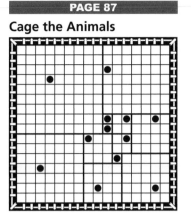

LETTERBLOCKS •
SQUARE / PYRAMID

PAGE 88

Letter Search #1

43 capitals, 33 lowercase, 6 red

PAGE 89

Check It Out!

G	E	N	R	E		T	I	S		F	A	S
U	N	F	E	D		A	P	T		A	B	C
Y	E	L	L	S		C	O	U	N	T	E	R
		E	E	K			C	A	S	T	E	
C	A	T	A	L	O	G		C	H	O	S	E
A	M	O	S		A	L	P	O				
B	Y	T	E		L	E	A		R	A	C	E
			S	A	N	D		O	V	A	L	
S	L	O	P	E		N	U	M	B	E	R	S
W	O	M	A	N		A	O	L				
O	V	E	R	D	U	E		P	O	P	U	P
R	E	G		E	S	S		E	W	O	K	S
E	R	A		R	A	P		D	E	W	E	Y

PAGE 90

Time

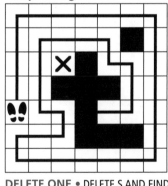

Time consists of a sequence of
moments. It is the fourth dimension
after height, width and length.

PAGE 91

Keep Going

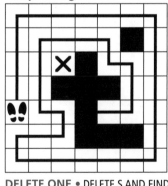

DELETE ONE • DELETE S AND FIND
DAILY NEWSPAPER.

PAGE 92

Golden Arches

S	A	M	E		S	T	A	R	R		E	M	I	L
A	L	E	X		C	A	N	O	E		A	C	R	E
F	I	L	E	T	O	F	I	S	H		S	C	A	N
E	N	T	R	A	N	T		S	E	E	T	H	E	D
R	E	S	C	U	E			A	M	O	I			
			I	P	S	O		C	R	U	N	C	H	Y
P	O	I	S	E		T	R	E	S	S		K	E	A
L	I	C	E		P	H	A	S	E		R	E	A	L
U	S	E		A	R	E	N	T		K	I	N	T	E
M	E	D	D	L	E	R		A	M	E	N			
		L	E	T	A			A	F	G	H	A	N	
I	T	A	L	I	C	S		T	R	I	T	O	N	E
R	A	T	E		H	A	S	H	B	R	O	W	N	S
M	I	T	T		E	N	R	O	L		S	T	A	T
A	L	E	E		S	T	A	R	E		S	O	N	S

PAGE 93

Number Cluster

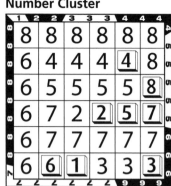

MISSING LETTER PROVERB •
A WATCHED POT NEVER BOILS.

PAGE 94

Spot the Differences

BLOCK ANAGRAM •
SOLAR PANEL

PAGE 95

Themeless

A	B	E	T		S	L	E	E	P		A	R	N	E
L	E	A	H		H	E	A	R	A		R	E	E	L
M	A	R	E		R	O	V	E	R		A	B	E	L
S	U	N	S	H	I	N	E		T	I	R	A	D	E
			P	U	M	A		T	I	N	A			
S	C	R	I	M	P		H	E	S	I	T	A	N	T
A	H	E	A	D		M	A	R	A	T		L	O	O
J	E	N	N	I	F	E	R	A	N	I	S	T	O	N
A	R	A		N	O	N	E	T		A	C	A	S	E
K	I	L	O	G	R	A	M		S	T	A	R	E	D
		N	E	W	T		P	E	E	L				
C	A	M	E	R	A		M	I	N	D	L	E	S	S
E	L	O	I		R	H	I	N	O		I	L	I	A
D	I	E	D		D	O	L	O	R		O	M	R	I
E	T	T	A		S	I	E	N	A		N	O	E	L

PAGE 96–97

What's Missing

1. D  4. C

2. C

3. D

Ladyug: Logic changes:
Row 1: Add the dots on the first two ladybugs to get the third;
Row 2: Subtract the dots on the second ladybug from the first to get the third; **Row 3:** Multiply the dots on the first two ladybugs to get the third.

PAGE 98

State Flags #2

L	O	R	D		E	L	M	S		B	A	T	E	S
E	R	I	E		A	E	R	O		O	P	E	N	S
M	I	N	N	E	S	O	T	A		O	R	N	O	T
A	B	S	T	A	I	N		P	I	N	O	N		
T	I	E		T	E	A	R		N	I	N	E	T	Y
		P	E	R		E	L	K	E		S	E	E	
E	D	W	I	N		E	D	I	E	S		S	S	A
D	R	I	P		S	C	R	O	D		C	E	L	S
G	A	S		S	W	O	O	N		T	R	E	A	T
A	C	C		T	A	L	C		T	R	Y			
R	O	O	M	E	R		K	E	R	I		A	S	H
		N	O	R	M	S		R	O	B	E	R	T	O
H	O	S	N	I		N	E	W	J	E	R	S	E	Y
A	R	I	E	L		A	D	I	A		G	O	A	L
M	O	N	T	E		P	E	N	N		O	N	M	E

PAGE 99

Write Me

C. Starting with the middle letter M, to the right and left all letters are always 1, 2, 3 and 4 places further in the alphabet.

END GAME •
(M I S S P E N D)
(F I E N D I S H)
(L E N D A B L E)
(E N D O C Y S T)

PAGE 100

Sport Maze

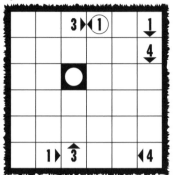

CHANGE ONE • HOT CAKES

ONE LETTER LESS OR MORE •
BADMINTON

PAGE 101

Spring

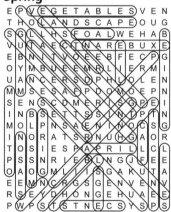

Even though we have become much less dependent on nature, spring makes everyone happy.

PAGE 102

Word Pyramid

F
(1) FA
(2) FAT
(3) FAST
(4) FACTS
(5) CRAFTS
(6) FACTORS
(7) FORECAST

State Birds

T	F	A	L		L	I	E	D		S	C	R	A	M
A	E	R	O		E	N	V	Y		T	O	O	N	E
C	H	I	C	K	A	D	E	E		E	R	A	T	O
O	R	L	A	N	D	O		S	L	E	N	D	E	R
		T	E	E			A	P	E	R				
A	A	M	I	L	N	E		C	U	L	T	U	R	E
I	S	E	N	T		T	R	A	D	E		N	O	D
S	T	A	G		S	H	A	P	E		S	N	U	G
L	E	D		P	H	A	S	E		S	C	E	N	E
E	R	O	S	I	O	N		R	E	C	O	R	D	S
		W	H	O	A				L	A	R			
A	T	L	A	N	T	A		S	U	R	P	A	S	S
U	K	A	S	E		G	O	L	D	F	I	N	C	H
T	O	R	T	E		E	L	I	E		O	T	O	E
O	S	K	A	R		D	A	D	S		N	I	P	S

Trivial Pursuit 1949

1. Joe DiMaggio
2. Toronto Maple Leafs
3. Joe Louis
4. New York Giants
5. Stan Musial

TEST YOUR RECALL • CADILLAC

Sudoku

4	2	7	1	6	3	5	9	8
5	9	6	8	7	2	1	4	3
3	1	8	9	5	4	7	2	6
2	3	5	6	8	1	4	7	9
1	6	9	5	4	7	3	8	2
8	7	4	3	2	9	6	1	5
6	4	1	2	3	8	9	5	7
9	8	3	7	1	5	2	6	4
7	5	2	4	9	6	8	3	1

Comic Book Heroes

U	N	S	E	R		S	C	A	D		H	U	L	K
R	E	P	A	Y		O	L	D	E		E	R	I	N
A	R	I	S	E		W	O	L	V	E	R	I	N	E
L	O	D	E			P	A	I	N		A	D	E	
		E	D	I	T	H		I	T	O		H	A	L
E	R	R		L	E	A	F		O	L	E			
D	E	M		L	A	U	R	A		A	D	I	O	S
A	D	A	Y		S	T	O	R	M		U	N	D	O
M	O	N	E	T		E	N	D	E	D		V	I	A
		S	R	I		T	O	N	E		I	N	K	
C	A	P		I	T	S		R	U	S	T	S		
A	P	O		A	S	A	P			R	I	L	L	
D	A	R	E	D	E	V	I	L		T	A	B	O	O
E	T	T	A		L	O	N	E		W	I	L	M	A
T	H	O	R		F	R	E	D		A	T	E	A	M

Binairo

I	O	I	O	I	O	I	I	O	I	O	O
O	I	O	I	O	I	I	O	I	O	O	I
O	O	I	I	O	I	O	O	I	O	I	I
I	I	O	O	I	O	I	I	O	I	O	O
O	O	I	I	O	I	O	I	I	O	I	O
O	I	I	O	I	O	I	O	O	I	O	I
I	O	O	I	O	I	O	I	O	O	I	I
O	O	I	O	I	I	O	I	I	O	I	O
I	I	O	I	O	O	I	O	O	I	O	I
O	I	O	I	I	O	O	I	O	I	I	O
I	O	I	O	O	I	O	O	I	O	I	I
I	I	O	O	I	O	I	O	I	I	O	O

REPOSITION PREPOSITION •
AS REGARDS

Cage the Animals

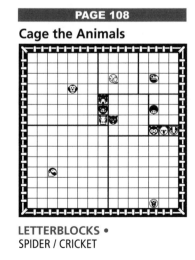

LETTERBLOCKS •
SPIDER / CRICKET

Animal Instincts

1. ailurophile—[A] lover of cats. Being an *ailurophile* is one thing, but building an entire wing for your feline friend is another.

2. leporine—[C] of or relating to a hare. "So much for the judges' *leporine* bias," boasted the tortoise as he studied the instant replay.

3. komondor—[A] Hungarian sheepdog. "Maybe I'll have your *komondor* do double duty as a kitchen mop!" Ms. Gulch growled.

4. Komodo dragon—[B] Indonesian lizard. The *Komodo dragon*'s name is justified: This carnivore is the heaviest living species of lizard in the world.

5. caudal—[C] tail-like. Waving her arms in a ludicrously *caudal* fashion, Ann did her best to illustrate the puppy's excitement.

6. stridulate—[C] make a shrill noise by rubbing together body structures, as a cricket does. The insects continued to *stridulate*, forcing sleep-deprived Fran to don earplugs.

7. clowder—[B] group of cats. Testing a new catnip recipe, Leslie fled the room pursued by a crazed *clowder*.

8. brindled—[A] streaky, as a coat. Camouflaged in her costume, Marti hid among the *brindled* barnyard cows.

9. card—[B] brush or disentangle fibers, as of wool. At the rate Beth is *carding* that yarn, she'll have half a sweater by Easter!

10. zoolatry—[A] animal worship. Do you think naming your cocker spaniel Your Majesty is taking *zoolatry* too far?

11. vibrissa—[A] whisker. Constantly hurrying, the nervous White Rabbit still took time to fuss over each *vibrissa*.

12. grimalkin—[C] old female cat. We weren't sure who was creepier: the old lady or the bedraggled *grimalkin* that always sat on her lap.

13. feral—[C] not domesticated. When Liz said, "Smile for the camera," her son bared his teeth like a *feral* hound.

14. cosset—[A] pamper or treat as a pet. Uncle Paul *cossets* his nieces. They don't have to lift a finger.

15. ethology—[C] study of animal behavior. Natalie needs to complete her *ethology* degree before she can join the monkey expedition.

VOCABULARY RATINGS
9 and below: something the cat dragged in
10–12: big fish
13–15: king of the forest

PAGE 110

Say Cheese!

PAGE 111

Kakuro

DOUBLETALK • ALTERNATE

MISSING LETTER PROVERB •
A MISS IS AS GOOD AS A MILE.

PAGE 112

Missing Plan

Cube 2

DOODLE PUZZLE • PIL**LOW**

PAGE 113

U.S. Cities

PAGE 114

Sudoku Twin

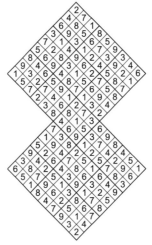

DOUBLETALK • STAFF

PAGE 115

Keep Going

DELETE ONE •
DELETE ONE S AND FIND PLATITUDES

PAGE 116

Cinema Classics

PAGE 117

France

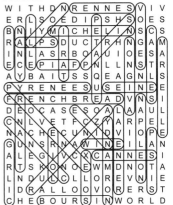

With diverse dishes such as bouillabaisse and cassoulet, French cuisine is known and loved all over the world.

PAGE 118

Ice Melt

162 thousand cubic kilometers.
The volume of ice always equals the
number of degrees multiplied by half.
18 x (18/2) = 162.

DOODLE PUZZLE • WORK PIECES

PAGE 119

Themeless

A	B	I	T		S	A	C	H	A		P	E	A	L
S	E	R	E		E	M	A	I	L		U	G	L	I
A	G	O	N		V	I	N	G	T		L	O	S	E
H	U	N	T	E	R	S	T	H	O	M	P	S	O	N
I	N	S	O	L	E	S		C	H	A	I			
		O	K	S		S	H	O	R	T	I	S	H	
B	E	R	N	E		T	E	A	R	S		M	O	E
A	R	O	E		D	I	G	I	N		S	I	M	I
T	I	M		S	A	N	E	R		M	E	T	E	R
S	K	E	L	E	T	A	L		L	O	A			
		A	R	A	B		M	I	S	S	I	L	E	
H	E	A	R	T	B	R	E	A	K	H	O	T	E	L
A	C	H	Y		A	O	R	T	A		N	A	V	I
T	H	O	N		S	W	I	S	S		A	L	E	S
S	T	Y	X		E	N	N	U	I		L	O	R	E

PAGE 120

A Cup of Joe

1. **c.** Forced out
2. **b.** Colombia and Brazil
3. **d.** A long-handled copper pot
   for making Turkish coffee
4. **c.** Made from coffee beans
   eaten and excreted by a
   Sumatran wildcat
5. **d.** Their ports of origin
6. **a.** The drink's resemblance to
   the brown cowls worn by
   Capuchin monks
7. **c.** Arabica and robusta beans
8. **b.** A bush
9. **b.** Freeze-dried
10. **a.** Its stimulating effects

PAGE 121

Canvas

Color 2. The areas with one, two,
three and four thick borders are
painted respectively green, blue,
yellow and red.

LETTER LINE • PILGRIMAGE;
IMPERIL, GARGLE, REGAL, GALE

PAGE 122

Word Sudoku

T	L	A	C	E	M	I	B	D
C	I	E	L	B	D	A	T	M
B	D	M	A	I	T	L	E	C
D	T	B	E	M	L	C	I	A
I	A	C	D	T	B	E	M	L
M	E	L	I	C	A	T	D	B
E	M	D	T	L	C	B	A	I
A	C	I	B	D	E	M	L	T
L	B	T	M	A	I	D	C	E

TRANSADDITION • ADD O AND N
AND FIND WESTERN UNION

PAGE 123

Sport Maze

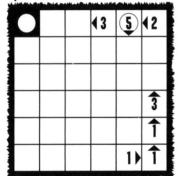

CHANGE ONE • HUMBLE PIE

ONE LETTER LESS OR MORE •
CHOLERA

PAGE 124

National Dairy Month

I	T	S	Y		E	T	A	L		A	G	T
R	E	P	O		C	O	L	A		D	U	E
S	N	A	G		H	O	L	S	T	E	I	N
			U	P	O	N			U	P	D	O
N	O	T	R	E		B	U	T	T	E	R	
U	N	I	T	E		K	I	N				
B	O	N		V	O	I	C	E		M	A	Y
			E	N	D		A	G	A	P	E	
C	H	E	E	S	E		S	E	C	T	S	
R	O	B	S			N	O	E	L			
I	C	E	C	R	E	A	M		A	C	R	E
S	U	R		A	L	M	A		T	U	B	S
P	S	T		M	I	E	N		O	D	I	E

PAGE 125

Sudoku X

4	2	8	7	1	9	6	5	3
3	7	9	6	2	5	8	4	1
6	5	1	3	4	8	2	9	7
9	6	4	5	3	7	1	8	2
2	1	7	9	8	4	3	6	5
8	3	5	1	6	2	4	7	9
7	8	6	2	5	3	9	1	4
1	9	2	4	7	6	5	3	8
5	4	3	8	9	1	7	2	6

SANDWICH • POWER

PAGE 126

Seedless

Tannin 1.40%. The sum of the five
other percentages equals 100%.
Grape pulp does not contain any
tannin.

END GAME •
(I N T E N D E D)
(F R I E N D L Y)
(B E N D A B L E)
(U N T E N D E D)

PAGE 127

Johnny Mercer Songs

S	E	A	S		R	O	S	E	S		A	M	P	S
A	N	N	A		I	N	T	R	O		S	O	L	E
P	S	I	L	O	V	E	Y	O	U		S	O	U	R
O	U	T	A	G	E	S		S	T	R	A	N	G	E
R	E	A	D	E	R			H	A	I	R			
			B	E	S	S		R	E	P	L	I	E	D
B	E	T	A	S		T	E	A	R	S		V	M	I
I	T	A	R		D	A	R	I	N		B	E	I	N
B	U	N		E	R	I	N	S		F	O	R	T	E
B	I	G	O	T	E	D		A	M	U	R			
			E	D	N	A			E	R	R	A	T	A
S	C	R	E	A	M	S		G	R	O	O	V	E	D
E	R	I	S		S	U	M	M	E	R	W	I	N	D
T	U	N	S		U	R	I	E	L		E	S	S	E
I	D	E	A		P	E	O	N	Y		D	O	E	R

Answers

PAGE 128

Trivial Pursuit 1937

1. Doc, Happy, Bashful, Sneezy, Sleepy, Grumpy, Dopey
2. Diamond mine
3. Dopey
4. False. Its only nomination was for score, which it did not win. In 1939, the Academy gave it a Special Award for "significant screen innovation."
5. True
6. C) 8, in '44, '52, '58, '67, '75, '83, '87 and '93.

TEST YOUR RECALL •
DUESENBERG SJ LA PHAETON

PAGE 129

Cage the Animals

LETTERBLOCKS • HURDLES / JAVELIN

PAGE 130

State-of-the-Art

W	O	L	F		G	A	P	E	D		H	O	N	E
A	R	I	L		A	G	O	R	A		O	D	I	E
R	E	M	O		L	A	N	A	I		R	O	L	L
M	O	N	O	P	O	L	Y	S	Q	U	A	R	E	S
			D	A	R				U	S	C			
R	E	T	I	R	E	S		D	I	S	E	A	S	E
E	D	E	N	S		W	E	A	R			F	E	N
S	I	N	G	E	R	E	R	N	I	E	F	O	R	D
E	T	S			E	D	G	E		D	R	O	V	E
T	H	E	B	A	B	E		S	E	D	A	T	E	D
		O	S	U			R	I	G					
A	S	H	I	P	T	O	R	E	M	E	M	B	E	R
N	O	E	L		T	R	E	V	I		E	R	N	E
I	D	L	E		E	L	L	E	N		N	I	N	E
L	A	P	D		D	O	Y	L	E		T	E	A	L

PAGE 131

Sudoku

1	5	4	8	3	7	6	2	9
9	7	8	6	2	1	3	5	4
2	6	3	9	4	5	7	8	1
5	3	6	1	9	4	8	7	2
8	2	1	7	5	3	4	9	6
4	9	7	2	6	8	1	3	5
7	4	2	5	8	6	9	1	3
6	8	5	3	1	9	2	4	7
3	1	9	4	7	2	5	6	8

FRIENDS • EACH CAN HAVE THE PREFIX ARCH- TO FORM A NEW WORD.

PAGE 132

Sunny

BLOCK ANAGRAM • CRUISE MISSILE

PAGE 133

Mellow Yellow

L	A	B			D	A	N	A		B	U	B	B	E
E	X	O		C	A	R	O	M		O	N	E	I	L
N	E	W	Y	O	R	K	T	A	X	I	C	A	B	S
A	L	L	E	N		A	I	D	E		L	U	B	E
			S	I	G	N		O	R	S	O			
F	R	E	N	C	H	S	M	U	S	T	A	R	D	
A	U	T	O		E	A	U		O	K	I	E	S	
D	N	H		L	E	N	S	C	A	P		C	E	E
S	I	N	A	I		I	L	O		O	K	R	A	
	C	O	M	M	O	N	C	A	N	A	R	I	E	S
		A	E	R	O		V	E	N	T				
I	C	A	N		A	M	B	I		G	H	A	N	A
D	A	F	F	O	D	I	L	C	O	L	O	R	E	D
E	R	R	O	R		N	O	L	T	E		U	M	A
S	P	O	R	T		A	B	E	T			M	O	M

PAGE 134

Number Cluster

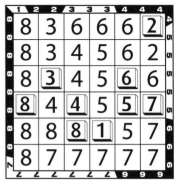

MISSING LETTER PROVERB •
KEEP YOUR POWDER DRY.

PAGE 135

Letter Search #2

28 capitals, 30 lowercase, 6 blue

PAGE 136

Frosty Airs

A	M	S		W	I	G	H	T		W	R	I	T	E
L	A	I		H	O	R	A	E		E	A	T	E	N
I	S	L		A	W	A	S	S	A	I	L	I	N	G
S	H	E	I	L	A	S		T	I	R	E			
T	A	N	N	I	N		C	O	R	D		J	E	T
		T	O	N		D	A	F	F	O	D	I	L	S
P	A	N		G	A	I	N		A	S	O	N	I	A
A	R	I	A		W	A	D	E	R		I	G	O	R
D	E	G	R	E	E		I	N	E	S		L	T	S
U	N	H	A	S	S	L	E	D		W	O	E		
A	T	T		C	O	E	D		B	A	R	B	E	R
			P	U	M	A		S	I	N	C	E	R	E
A	C	C	I	D	E	N	T	A	L	S		L	E	E
P	H	O	N	O		T	A	N	G	O		L	C	D
T	E	X	A	S		O	L	S	E	N		S	T	S

244

245

PAGE 137

Binairo

O	I	O	O	I	I	O	I	I	O	I
I	O	I	O	I	O	I	O	I	O	O	I	I
I	I	O	I	O	I	O	I	I	O	O
O	O	I	I	O	I	I	O	O	I	I
I	I	O	O	I	O	I	O	I	I	O
O	O	I	I	O	I	O	I	I	O	I
O	O	I	O	I	I	O	I	O	I	I
I	I	O	I	I	O	I	O	O	I	O
O	I	I	O	O	I	O	I	I	O	I
I	O	I	I	O	O	I	I	O	I	O
I	I	O	I	I	O	I	O	I	O	O

REPOSITION PREPOSITION •
THANKS TO

PAGE 138

Spot the Differences

PAGE 139

Summer Picnic

A	C	D	C		G	A	I	N		B	O	B
N	O	A	H		A	L	S	O		E	L	L
G	O	B	I		L	E	M	O	N	A	D	E
		C	H	E	X		S	A	L	E	S	
B	R	A	K	E	S		R	E	P	E	N	T
R	I	P	E	N		H	A	S				
O	M	E	N		J	I	G		B	A	T	S
		C	O	D		E	L	I	O	T		
R	A	B	B	I	T		G	R	A	M	M	Y
A	G	A	I	N		Y	U	A	N			
B	A	R	B	E	C	U	E		K	A	L	E
I	P	O		M	A	R	S		E	D	E	N
D	E	N		A	N	T	S		T	O	A	D

PAGE 140

Keep Going

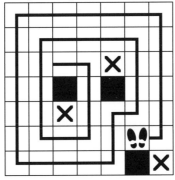

DELETE ONE •
DELETE A AND FIND SORE THROAT

PAGE 141

Exercise

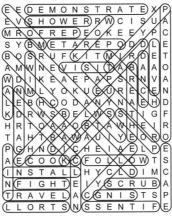

Exercise keeps you fit and keeps your body weight within healthy limits.

PAGE 142

How Sweet!

L	A	N	G		A	B	A	S	H		M	E	G	S
A	L	I	I		R	A	D	I	I		O	R	L	E
P	A	L	M		C	R	I	B	S		U	S	E	E
P	I	E	C	H	A	R	T		T	E	S	T	E	R
			R	U	N	E		S	O	D	S			
P	A	N	A	D	A		S	H	R	I	E	K	E	D
I	R	O	C		A	W	A	I	T		L	A	O	
C	O	O	K	I	E	G	I	L	C	H	R	I	S	T
O	S	S		C	L	O	N	E		A	N	T	E	
T	E	E	T	H	I	N	G		R	E	C	E	S	S
			R	O	S	Y		W	A	V	E			
L	A	H	I	R	I		C	A	K	E	W	A	L	K
U	S	A	F		O	M	A	N	I		A	L	A	N
G	I	L	L		N	I	N	E	S		Y	O	K	E
E	A	S	E		S	T	A	S	H		S	T	E	W

PAGE 143

Word Sudoku

R	O	U	V	D	P	E	W	C
D	E	C	O	R	W	P	V	U
W	V	P	C	U	E	D	O	R
E	U	O	R	W	V	C	D	P
P	D	R	U	O	C	W	E	V
C	W	V	P	E	D	R	U	O
V	R	E	D	C	O	U	P	W
U	P	W	E	V	R	O	C	D
O	C	D	W	P	U	V	R	E

UNCANNY TURN •
CLAUDE DEBUSSY

PAGE 144

Sudoku

1	6	3	5	4	9	7	8	2
4	7	2	1	8	6	3	9	5
5	9	8	2	7	3	1	4	6
7	1	6	9	5	4	8	2	3
2	5	4	7	3	8	9	6	1
8	3	9	6	1	2	4	5	7
3	8	5	4	2	7	6	1	9
9	4	1	3	6	5	2	7	8
6	2	7	8	9	1	5	3	4

PAGE 145

Pairing Up

FIT THE PIECES

LOCK TOGETHER

PAGE 146

Sport Maze

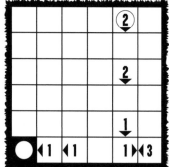

CHANGE ONE •
SHOUTING MATCH

ONE LETTER LESS OR MORE •
AMAZING

PAGE 147

Themeless

M	A	R	I	S		S	P	A	T		D	I	S	S
A	L	O	N	E		T	A	C	H		E	T	C	H
R	A	T	H	E		I	N	T	E	R	F	E	R	E
V	I	T	A	M	I	N	S		R	O	A	M	E	D
		E	L	E	C	T		R	E	B	U	S	E	S
L	A	R	E	D	O		E	A	S	E	L			
E	N	D	S		N	U	B	I	A		T	A	C	O
A	D	A		L	B	S			T	O	D			
H	Y	M	N		K	N	E	E	D		H	A	L	E
		I	L	I	A	D		A	M	E	N	D	S	
O	B	S	C	E	N	E		D	I	A	R	Y		
N	A	T	H	A	N		H	I	S	T	O	R	I	C
E	R	R	O	N	E	O	U	S		T	I	A	R	A
A	R	I	L		A	V	E	C		E	N	T	E	R
L	E	A	S		R	O	Y	S		R	E	E	D	S

PAGE 148

Best Picture

O	D	O	R		R	A	C	E		S	W	A	N
L	A	M	E		A	B	O	V	E		T	A	M	I
A	N	N	A		D	O	Z	E	N		E	T	O	N
F	A	I	R	L	A	D	Y		R	E	V	E	R	E
			O	R	E		N	A	D	E	R			
A	S	C	O	T	S		L	O	G	E		F	E	E
L	E	A	P	S		R	O	U	E	N		R	A	V
L	A	S	T		S	O	U	N	D		R	O	S	A
E	T	A		A	M	A	S	S		W	A	N	E	D
N	O	B		B	O	D	Y		R	A	T	T	L	E
		L	E	E	K	S		C	I	D				
C	H	A	S	T	E		G	O	N	E	W	I	T	H
R	U	N	T		R	O	A	N	S		A	C	R	E
O	N	C	E		S	N	I	D	E		S	E	E	M
P	T	A	S		E	N	O	S		P	E	E	P	

PAGE 149

Cage the Animals

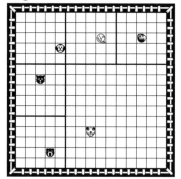

LETTERBLOCKS •
LINCOLN / MERCURY

PAGE 150

Constellation

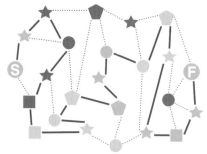

PAGE 151

TV Westerns

L	I	F	E		B	A	L	D		P	A	V	E	D
A	R	I	D		A	R	E	A		O	L	I	V	E
V	I	R	G	I	N	I	A	N		M	E	D	E	A
A	S	S	E	T		D	E	E	M		A	R	T	
		R	E	B	S		S	T	E	A	L	T	H	
G	U	N	S	M	O	K	E		A	L	L			
A	T	E		S	H	I	P	S		A	M	E	S	
B	A	R	D		R	E	S	O	D		S	A	R	I
S	H	O	E		S	O	L	E	D		G	I	N	
		L	E	E		M	A	V	E	R	I	C	K	
W	I	D	E	N	E	D		R	O	L	E			
A	M	A		C	L	E	F		T	A	S	T	E	
G	A	R	B	O		B	I	G	V	A	L	L	E	Y
O	G	L	E	R		I	D	E	A		T	U	N	E
N	E	A	L	E		T	O	O	T		Y	E	N	S

PAGE 152

Languages

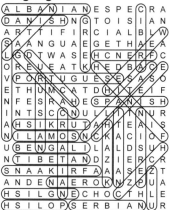

Esperanto is an artificial language that was created so that different cultures could understand each other.

PAGE 153

Number Block

7. Every number equals the sum of the number of blocks to the right of the number and the number of blocks under the number.

END GAME •
(A S C E N D E R)
(U N B E N D E D)
(R E M E N D E D)
(A M E N D F U L)

PAGE 154

Case Crackers

E	C	H	O		L	I	L	L	I		S	N	O	W
D	R	I	P		O	N	E	I	L		L	A	M	A
G	I	D	E	O	N	F	E	L	L		E	N	O	S
A	M	E	R	I	G	O		T	I	M	E	C	O	P
R	E	S	A	L	E			N	A	V	Y			
			T	E	R	N		B	O	R	E	D	O	M
A	B	L	E	R		E	L	L	I	S		R	U	E
L	E	A	S		C	I	T	E	S		V	E	S	T
E	A	U		H	O	L	D	S		N	E	W	T	S
C	U	R	E	A	L	L		S	C	A	N			
		A	R	I	L			R	H	E	T	O	R	
B	A	H	A	M	A	S		T	A	U	R	I	N	E
E	R	O	S		P	E	R	R	Y	M	A	S	O	N
N	I	L	E		S	A	N	Y	O		T	H	U	D
S	E	T	S		E	T	H	A	N		E	A	R	S

PAGE 155

Kakuro

2	9	3	■	9	7	2	■	4
7	■	1	6	5	9	■	1	5
■	9	6	8	■	4	8	2	6
7	2	8	■	■	1	3	■	9
1	■	2	1	5	■	1	5	7
6	2	■	9	7	1	■	3	■
■	7	6	■	9	■	1	9	■
7	6	2	8	4	■	1	4	■
5	8	■	9	1	■	2	7	1

DOUBLETALK • SECOND

MISSING LETTER PROVERB •
BARKING DOGS SELDOM BITE.

PAGE 156

Keep Going

DELETE ONE • DELETE L AND FIND
COUNTERFEITER

PAGE 157

Spanning the Spectrum

P	L	U	M	■	H	E	R	O	■	A	P	P
T	U	N	A	■	O	V	E	R	■	F	U	R
A	G	O	G	■	S	A	P	P	H	I	R	E
■	■	E	D	E	N	■	H	O	R	S	E	■
C	O	R	N	E	A	■	S	A	T	E	E	N
A	B	A	T	E	■	T	A	N	■	■	■	■
N	I	N	A	■	W	A	X	■	C	H	I	P
■	■	■	R	E	D	■	B	R	A	C	E	■
A	B	R	O	A	D	■	W	A	I	T	E	R
G	L	A	N	D	■	R	O	A	M	■	■	■
L	A	V	E	N	D	E	R	■	S	A	R	A
E	R	E	■	E	O	N	S	■	O	V	E	N
T	E	N	■	R	O	O	T	■	N	A	V	Y

PAGE 158-159

Color Travels

DISCO LIGHTS

KALEIDOMAZE

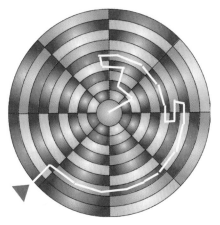

PAGE 160

Doctor Who

A	M	O	S	■	T	R	O	I	K	A	■	B	E	D
S	O	R	A	■	H	A	S	S	A	N	■	U	N	A
S	T	E	L	S	E	W	H	E	R	E	■	R	O	Y
T	O	O	T	O	O	■	A	A	A	■	A	N	K	A
■	■	■	I	A	M	S	■	S	T	A	R	S	I	N
F	R	A	N	K	E	N	S	T	E	I	N	■	■	■
A	I	D	E	■	G	O	O	■	■	N	E	G	E	V
I	N	A	■	L	A	B	C	O	A	T	■	U	R	I
R	O	M	E	O	■	■	K	A	N	■	P	R	O	S
■	■	■	G	R	E	G	O	R	Y	H	O	U	S	E
R	O	M	A	I	N	E	■	S	O	A	P	■	■	■
A	B	C	D	■	S	A	W	■	T	R	O	J	A	N
P	E	C	■	Y	U	R	I	Z	H	I	V	A	G	O
I	S	O	■	B	R	U	L	E	E	■	E	V	E	R
D	E	Y	■	K	E	P	L	E	R	■	R	A	R	A

PAGE 161

Parking Space

Car 11. All white and red cars are
parked nose inward. All blue cars are
parked with the nose outward except
car 11.

LETTER LINE • MOUSETRAPS;
MAESTRO, TAMPER, STREAM,
MASTER

PAGE 162

Sudoku

4	2	7	3	9	6	8	5	1
9	8	3	5	7	1	6	2	4
5	6	1	8	2	4	9	7	3
3	1	2	9	5	7	4	8	6
6	4	9	2	1	8	5	3	7
8	7	5	6	4	3	2	1	9
1	9	8	7	6	2	3	4	5
7	3	6	4	8	5	1	9	2
2	5	4	1	3	9	7	6	8

PAGE 163

Bright Lights

Candle C. Place the factors 1, 2 and 3
on the right colors then add up each
candle. 5-6-4-6-6-7.

LETTER LINE • CONSTRAINT;
CARTONS, CONTRAST, ANTICS, TINT

Answers

PAGE 164

Flag It

Flag M. Every pair includes a red and white flag. The other flag in the pair has the same pattern, but all the colors are different. Only one color is different on flag M.

END GAME •
(F O R E F E N D)
(E X P E N D E R)
(L E G E N D R Y)
(E N D O G E N Y)

PAGE 165

On the Beach

A	P	B		P	U	C	E			C	L	A	M
M	O	A		O	S	H	E	A		S	A	O	N	E
I	L	K		S	H	E	L	L	I	N	G	O	U	T
S	K	E	E	T	E	R		I	M	A	Y		
H	A	R	P	E	R		D	E	P	P		U	S	K
		S	I	R		P	I	N	E	A	P	P	L	E
K	I	D		S	A	R	G		A	T	T	A	I	N
E	N	O	S		L	O	G	I	C		A	N	D	Y
O	F	Z	E	A	L		E	C	H	O		D	E	A
G	R	E	A	T	F	I	R	E		N	S	A		
H	A	N		O	R	B	S		D	E	G	R	E	E
		I	D	E	A		T	R	I	T	O	N	S	
C	H	O	W	D	E	R	H	E	A	D		U	L	T
E	U	R	O	S		S	E	L	M	A		N	A	E
L	E	O	N			P	E	A	S		D	I	S	

PAGE 166

Sport Maze

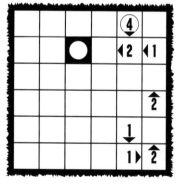

CHANGE ONE • WORK OUT

ONE LETTER LESS OR MORE • IGNORANCE

PAGE 167

Sunny

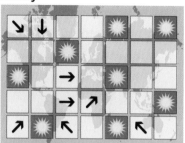

BLOCK ANAGRAM • IRONING BOARD

PAGE 168

Endangered Birds

E	S	M	E		A	L	I	V	E		A	B	C	S
T	H	E	M		V	E	N	A	L		F	L	A	P
H	A	R	P	Y	E	A	G	L	E		R	A	G	E
O	R	C	H	A	R	D		S	P	L	I	C	E	D
S	P	E	A	R	S			H	A	C	K			
		S	N	E	E		B	A	V	A	R	I	A	
L	E	W	I	S		L	I	A	N	A		A	D	D
I	D	O	S		S	C	A	N	T		M	I	L	E
A	G	O		S	T	I	N	G		G	A	L	E	N
R	E	D	F	O	R	D		S	P	U	R			
		S	E	T	A			R	A	C	I	A	L	
D	E	T	R	O	I	T		R	E	V	E	N	G	E
O	L	O	R		G	R	E	Y	F	A	L	C	O	N
S	A	R	I		H	O	R	N	E		L	A	R	I
E	L	K	S		T	I	G	E	R		O	N	A	N

PAGE 169

Mathematics

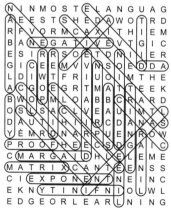

In most languages the word for mathematics is derived from the Greek word máthèma, which means science, knowledge or learning.

PAGE 170

Cage the Animals

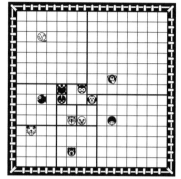

LETTERBLOCKS • BLOSSOM / COMPOST

PAGE 171

Science Diction

1. grok—[A] understand profoundly; coined by sci-fi pioneer Robert A. Heinlein. Elspeth *grokked* the oceans and was able to manipulate their currents.

2. psionic—[A] having paranormal ability. Artie wasn't surprised to see Tara move the pen using her *psionic* powers.

3. Chimera—[B] mythological monster. "It's half man, half horse?" the student offered up. "You're thinking of the centaur," the professor said. "The *Chimera* is part lion, goat, and serpent."

4. chrononaut—[C] time traveler. Who is your favorite *chrononaut*— Wells's Time Traveller, or Marty McFly?

5. draconic—[A] of or relating to a dragon. "What was the name of Pete's *draconic* friend in that kids' movie?" Lauren asked.

6. sapient—[C] keen, discerning. "I believe it was Elliott," her *sapient* friend Jules shot back.

7. terraform—[B] alter an environment so it can support life. After graduation, Dean's room will have to be *terraformed* before anyone else can move in.

8. cryonics—[A] practice of freezing a dead person in hopes of later restoring life. Before Ted Williams's relatives used *cryonics*, they faced a legal firestorm.

9. lycanthropic—[B] of or relating to werewolves. After a series of *lycanthropic* dreams, Tom sought advice from his doctor.

10. selenology—[C] study of the moon. Perhaps you shouldn't take up *selenology* if you're that afraid of werewolves.

11. dystopia—[B] nightmarish society. With all its freaks and geeks, Beth compared her office to the *dystopia* of Orwell's *Nineteen Eighty-Four*.

12. android—[A] robot with a human shape. A *Star Wars* fan's favorite *android*? We'd have to guess C-3PO.

13. cyborg—[C] bionic human. Steve Austin, *The Six Million Dollar Man*, was the most famous *cyborg* of the '70s.

14. telluric—[A] of or relating to the earth. Aboard ship, the docile aliens were eager to hear Alec's *telluric* tales.

PAGE 172

Tiny Circles

PAGE 173

Endangered Mammals

PAGE 174

Word Sudoku

S	W	Y	E	R	C	U	T	A
U	E	A	S	T	W	Y	C	R
R	T	C	U	Y	A	E	W	S
A	C	E	R	U	S	T	Y	W
T	R	S	W	E	Y	C	A	U
Y	U	W	C	A	T	R	S	E
E	S	T	Y	W	R	A	U	C
C	Y	U	A	S	E	W	R	T
W	A	R	T	C	U	S	E	Y

TRANSADDITION •
ADD A AND FIND WAITRESS

PAGE 175

Spot the Differences

PAGE 176

'50s Music Legends

PAGE 177

Sudoku Twin

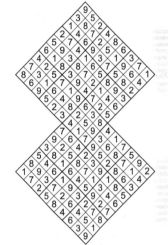

DOUBLETALK • DESERT

PAGE 178

Number Cluster

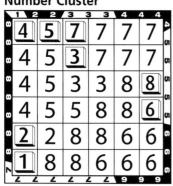

MISSING LETTER PROVERB • ALL GOOD THINGS MUST COME TO AN END.

PAGE 179

Sudoku

5	8	3	7	1	9	2	6	4
6	9	4	3	2	8	5	7	1
1	7	2	4	6	5	9	3	8
7	4	8	2	5	6	3	1	9
9	3	5	8	7	1	6	4	2
2	1	6	9	4	3	8	5	7
8	6	9	1	3	7	4	2	5
3	2	7	5	8	4	1	9	6
4	5	1	6	9	2	7	8	3

PAGE 180

Letter Search #3

10 capitals, 32 lowercase, 7 green

PAGE 181

Festivities

PAGE 182

Biology

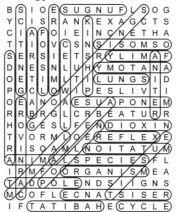

Biology is an exact science that studies living creatures, forms of life and signs of life.

PAGE 183

Keep Going

DELETE ONE • DELETE ONE S AND FIND ANCIENTS

PAGE 184

Sea Shanties

PAGE 185

Cubism

Group 2. In all the other groups two identically colored cubes are located diagonally across from each other in the corners.

LETTER LINE • INTRODUCE; REDUCTION, INDUCE, CONDUIT, RUINED

PAGE 186

Sudoku X

9	5	4	8	7	6	2	3	1
3	1	8	2	5	9	6	4	7
2	6	7	4	1	3	8	5	9
7	4	9	6	2	5	3	1	8
5	8	6	9	3	1	4	7	2
1	2	3	7	4	8	9	6	5
4	3	2	1	9	7	5	8	6
8	9	1	5	6	4	7	2	3
6	7	5	3	8	2	1	9	4

SANDWICH • SLEEP

PAGE 187

Cars

Increasingly stricter environmental laws force car manufacturers to look for alternative sources of energy.

PAGE 188

Odd Number

9. All other numbers are composed of a number of blocks equal to the value of the number.

DOODLE PUZZLE • FATSDOMINO

PAGE 189

Trivial Pursuit 1967

1. Alice's Restaurant, Arlo Guthrie

2. Are You Experienced? Jimi Hendrix ("Purple Haze")

3. Procol Harum ("Whiter Shade of Pale")

4. Disraeli Gears, Cream ("Sunshine of Your Love")

5. The Doors (Jim Morrison)

6. Surrealistic Pillow, Jefferson Airplane ("Somebody to Love," "White Rabbit")

TEST YOUR RECALL •
PONTIAC FIREBIRD

PAGE 190

Best-Sellers #2

PAGE 191

Word Sudoku

R	T	I	W	F	C	S	D	E
S	E	F	R	D	I	T	C	W
D	W	C	E	S	T	R	I	F
C	I	S	T	W	R	E	F	D
F	D	E	C	I	S	W	R	T
T	R	W	D	E	F	C	S	I
W	F	D	S	R	E	I	T	C
I	C	R	F	T	W	D	E	S
E	S	T	I	C	D	F	W	R

UNCANNY TURN •
HARRY POTTER

PAGE 192

Sudoku

4	1	8	5	9	2	6	7	3
7	6	9	4	1	3	5	2	8
3	2	5	7	6	8	1	4	9
8	3	4	2	7	6	9	5	1
2	5	7	9	8	1	4	3	6
6	9	1	3	5	4	7	8	2
9	7	2	1	3	5	8	6	4
5	8	3	6	4	9	2	1	7
1	4	6	8	2	7	3	9	5

PAGE 193

Stargazing

PAGE 194–195

Pentathlon

EASY READING • 28.
There are four ways of reaching the Ys in the corner of the diamond, and three ways each of reaching any of the eight Ys along the sides of the diamond. Thus: $(1 \times 4) + (3 \times 8) = 28$.

DICE TOWER • 19.
Since the opposite faces of a dice always add up to 7, the total must be $(4 \times 7) - 6 - 3 = 19$.

ONE INTO TWO

UNFINISHED WORK • 50.
As there are four blocks along the top, the smallest cube that can be constructed is $4 \times 4 \times 4 = 64$ blocks. As there are 14 blocks in position already, 50 more blocks are required to construct a solid cube.

UPHILL STRUGGLE • D (because gravity is a downward force).

Answers

PAGE 196

Relaxation

A	C	E	D		M	O	N	O		A	B	O	M	B
L	O	R	I		E	B	A	Y		M	O	V	I	E
T	H	E	S	U	N	I	S	S	H	I	N	I	N	G
O	N	I	O	N			A	T	A		A	D	E	S
		W	I	S	H		E	V	E	N				
	G	E	N	T	L	E	B	R	E	E	Z	E	S	
A	R	T	S		A	R	A			K	A	L	E	L
R	A	H		D	W	A	Y	N	E	S		I	D	A
K	I	N	T	E		O	E	R		D	O	G	S	
	L	O	W	E	R	H	U	M	I	D	I	T	Y	
	I	D	E	A		O	K	R	A					
E	G	A	N		I	R	K		A	M	E	B	A	
B	R	O	K	E	N	L	A	W	N	M	O	W	E	R
B	E	N	I	N		O	T	I	C		N	E	A	L
S	W	E	E	T		W	E	G	O		D	R	N	O

PAGE 197

Word Pyramid

A

(1) EA
(2) SEA
(3) SALE
(4) LEASE
(5) ASLEEP
(6) RELAPSE
(7) PLEASURE

PAGE 198–199

Word Ladders

1. MITE, MATE, MATS
2. NIL, NIP, NAP, GAP
3. POOL, POLL, PALL, PALE, PAGE
4. SEARS, STARS, STARE, STALE, STILE
5. HAND, HARD, HARE, FARE, FORE, FORT, FOOT
6. ARMS, AIMS, DIMS, DAMS, DAME, NAME, NAVE
7. GLUE, GLUT, GOUT, POUT, PORT, PART, PANT, PINT

REPOSITION PREPOSTION •
NOTWITHSTANDING

PAGE 200

Binairo

O	I	O	I	O	I	I	O	I	O	I	O
O	O	I	I	O	I	I	O	I	O	O	I
I	O	I	O	I	O	O	I	O	I	I	O
I	I	O	I	O	I	O	O	I	I	O	O
O	I	I	O	I	O	I	O	I	O	O	I
I	O	O	I	I	O	O	I	O	I	I	O
I	O	I	O	O	I	O	O	I	O	I	I
O	I	O	O	I	O	I	I	O	I	O	I
I	I	O	O	I	I	O	I	O	I	I	O
O	O	I	I	O	O	I	I	O	O	I	I
O	I	O	I	O	O	I	I	O	O	I	I
I	O	I	O	I	O	I	I	O	I	O	O

REPOSITION PREPOSTION •
ASIDE FROM

PAGE 201

First Name Last

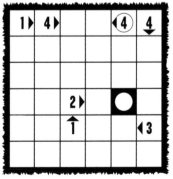

E	G	G	S		C	O	H	O		A	S	H	E	R
M	O	R	E		A	R	I	A		S	A	U	C	Y
B	L	A	C	K	J	A	C	K		P	I	N	T	A
E	D	I	T	I	O	N		S	K	E	L	T	O	N
D	A	N	I	E	L		E	C	O	L				
		O	L	E	S		E	N	T	R	I	E	S	
S	I	G	N		D	W	E	L	T		S	N	A	P
W	A	R			U	R	L			D	R	Y		
I	G	E	T		A	N	G	E	R		L	A	S	S
T	O	E	R	I	N	G		N	E	N	E			
		N	A	N	G		B	A	A	B	A	A		
V	I	S	I	T	E	D		P	E	R	S	O	N	S
I	R	E	N	E		R	O	C	K	C	H	R	I	S
L	A	T	E	R		A	B	B	A		E	N	S	E
A	S	H	E	N		G	I	S	H		D	E	E	T

PAGE 202

Sport Maze

CHANGE ONE • GREEN FINGERS

ONE LETTER LESS OR MORE •
DRUMBEATS

PAGE 203

Agriculture

Agriculture produces food as well as other goods such as flowers, fur, leather and biofuel.

PAGE 204

Last Name First

H	A	R	D		S	T	A	R	R		A	W	L	S
O	B	O	E		T	H	R	E	E		G	H	A	T
L	I	T	T	L	E	R	I	C	H		A	I	D	E
D	E	C	E	I	V	E	D		E	A	S	T	E	R
		S	K	E	W		M	A	N	S	E			
C	A	C	T	U	S		C	A	R	N	I	V	A	L
A	C	H	E	D		W	O	R	S	E		A	D	E
R	O	A	D		S	I	N	G	E		F	N	M	A
O	D	S		R	E	N	E	E		C	A	N	E	S
M	E	E	T	I	N	G	S		P	L	I	A	N	T
		C	R	O	S	S		H	A	I	R			
T	A	H	I	T	I		R	E	I	M	P	O	S	E
A	L	E	X		B	R	O	W	N	B	L	A	I	R
L	E	V	I		L	U	M	E	T		A	H	A	B
K	A	Y	E		E	G	A	D	S		Y	U	L	E

PAGE 205
Keep Going

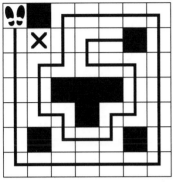

DELETE ONE •
DELETE A AND FIND SOMERSAULT

PAGE 206
Kakuro

DOUBLETALK • BANK

MISSING LETTER PROVERB •
IT IS BETTER TO GIVE THAN RECEIVE.

PAGE 207
Cage the Animals

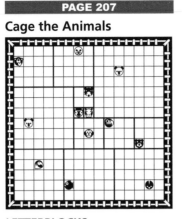

LETTERBLOCKS •
ENGLAND / GERMANY

PAGE 208
Sudoku

5	9	2	4	6	8	7	3	1
8	7	1	9	5	3	6	4	2
3	4	6	7	1	2	9	8	5
6	1	7	2	3	9	4	5	8
2	8	4	5	7	1	3	9	6
9	5	3	8	4	6	1	2	7
1	6	9	3	2	5	8	7	4
7	2	8	6	9	4	5	1	3
4	3	5	1	8	7	2	6	9

FRIENDS • EACH CAN HAVE THE
PREFIX DIA- TO FORM A NEW WORD.

PAGE 209
County Fair

PAGE 210–211
Stack Tracking

PAGE 212
Vintage Electronics

C	A	I	N		A	S	A	P		Q	U	I	T	S
O	C	T	A		R	O	M	A		U	P	S	E	T
R	C	A	V	I	C	T	O	R		A	S	A	N	A
A	T	L	A	S			K	I	S	S		A	S	K
			J	E	D	I		S	E	A		C	E	E
M	O	T	O	R	O	L	A		E	R	G			
I	N	A		E	N	O	L	A			A	S	I	A
L	U	N	G		E	V	A	N	S		S	L	A	P
A	S	S	N			E	R	N	E	S		A	G	E
			U	Z	I		M	A	G	N	A	V	O	X
C	D	S		E	T	C		L	A	I	R			
O	R	T		N	O	O	N			T	R	A	M	S
H	A	I	T	I		P	A	N	A	S	O	N	I	C
E	C	L	A	T		E	V	I	L		W	A	C	O
N	O	T	C	H		D	E	L	L		S	T	E	T

PAGE 213
In the Swim

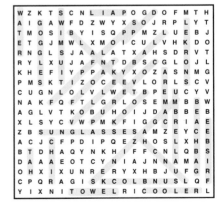

Answers

PAGE 214

Photography

The word *photography* is derived from Greek; it literally means "writing with light."

PAGE 215

Christmas Quiz

1. **c.** "White Christmas"
2. **a.** "Have Yourself a Merry Little Christmas"
3. **c.** "The Christmas Song"
4. **b.** "I Saw Mommy Kissing Santa Claus"
5. **b.** "Santa Baby"
6. **a.** "Jingle Bell Rock"
7. **c.** "Blue Christmas"
8. **b.** "Rockin' Around the Christmas Tree"
9. **c.** "Santa Looked a Lot Like Daddy"
10. **a.** "Holly Jolly Christmas"

PAGE 216

Sudoku

FRIENDS • EACH CAN HAVE THE PREFIX TRANS- TO FORM A NEW WORD.

PAGE 217

Winter Warm-Ups

A	P	P	S		S	T	E	W		F	O	R
C	L	A	W		H	E	R	O		I	F	I
E	Y	R	E		E	A	R	M	U	F	F	S
		A	J	A	R		B	R	E	A	K	
D	I	E	T	E	R		F	A	I	R	L	Y
O	C	T	E	T		J	U	T				
W	E	A	R		P	I	N		F	R	A	Y
		R	A	G		E	L	A	T	E		
A	S	S	A	I	L		G	R	A	P	E	S
S	H	A	R	P		B	R	A	N			
H	O	T	C	O	C	O	A		N	A	S	A
E	P	A		F	I	A	T		E	R	I	C
S	S	N		F	I	R	E		L	E	N	T

PAGE 218

Sunny

BLOCK ANAGRAM • SLEEPING ROOM

PAGE 219

Word Sudoku

S	A	M	X	P	N	R	O	T
N	P	R	O	A	T	X	S	M
X	T	O	S	R	M	P	N	A
M	O	N	R	X	A	T	P	S
A	S	P	M	T	O	N	R	X
R	X	T	P	N	S	A	M	O
O	N	X	A	S	P	M	T	R
T	R	S	N	M	X	O	A	P
P	M	A	T	O	R	S	X	N

UNCANNY TURN • INDIRA GANDHI

PAGE 220

An Old-Fashioned Christmas

PAGE 221

Know the Ropes

1. No—this is easily seen to be a simple loop if you imagine the right-hand end moved across to the left.
2. Yes—this is the simplest knot possible and is called a "trefoil knot."
3. Yes—this is another trefoil knot. However, notice that the knot is oriented differently from the previous knot. Knots, like people, are "right-handed" or "left-handed."
4. No—the large loop at the bottom will slip through the

hole in the middle, and this will become a straight piece of rope.

5. Yes
6. No
7. No
8. Yes.
9. No

PAGE 222

Pop Music

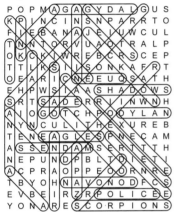

Pop music is part of a new cultural perception after the war, in which culture became the public property of everyone.

PAGE 223

Sudoku Twin

					1			

(Sudoku Twin diamond grid)

DOUBLETALK • APPROPRIATE

PAGE 224

Painter

Paint 3. 6/8 of a square was colored in with paints 1 and 4, 5/8 of a square for paint 2 and 7/8 for paint 3.

BLOCK ANAGRAM • SPINAL CORD

PAGE 225

Binairo

I	I	0	I	0	0	I	I	0	0	I	0
I	I	0	I	0	I	I	0	0	I	0	0
0	0	I	0	I	I	0	0	I	I	0	I
0	I	I	0	I	0	0	I	I	0	I	0
I	0	0	I	0	0	I	I	0	I	I	0
I	0	I	0	I	I	0	0	I	0	0	I
0	I	I	0	0	I	I	0	0	I	0	I
0	I	0	I	I	0	0	I	0	I	I	0
I	0	0	I	0	I	0	0	I	0	I	I
0	0	I	0	I	0	I	I	0	I	0	I
0	I	I	0	0	I	I	0	I	0	I	0
I	0	0	I	I	0	0	I	I	0	0	I

REPOSITION PREPOSITION • IN POINT OF

PAGE 226

Kakuro

TRANSADDITION • ADD S AND FIND CREDENTIALS

DOUBLETALK • STICK

PAGE 227

Wines

B	E	E	T		A	M	B	E	R		S	P	O	T
E	R	S	E		R	E	E	S	E		H	I	D	E
A	N	T	A		T	A	R	T	S		E	N	I	D
R	I	E	S	L	I	N	G		O	N	I	O	N	S
D	E	E	P	E	S	T		B	U	I	L	T		
		O	A	T		M	O	N	T	A	N	A	N	
L	U	Z	O	N		F	O	O	D	S		O	N	O
O	L	I	N		C	A	P	E	S		S	I	N	O
C	A	N		A	I	D	E	D		A	K	R	O	N
I	N	F	O	R	M	E	D		C	L	I			
	A	L	I	A	S		R	O	L	L	E	R	S	
T	I	N	D	E	R		S	E	M	I	L	L	O	N
A	N	D	I		R	E	C	A	P		F	A	L	A
T	R	E	E		O	V	A	T	E		U	T	E	P
A	I	L	S		N	A	T	A	L		L	E	S	S

PAGE 228

Motor Mania

1. 53
2. Bananas—as in the film *Herbie Goes Bananas*
3. It was the first land vehicle to break the sound barrier
4. Volvo
5. Aston Martin DB5
6. Rolls-Royce
7. Starsky and Hutch
8. The Model T Ford
9. Karl
10. A Delorean
11. National Association for Stock Car Auto Racing
12. Volkswagen Bug
13. Porsche 550 Spyder
14. General Lee, 1969 Orange Dodge Charger
15. 1955 Ford Lincoln Futura
16. A P-51 World War II Fighter Aircraft
17. Rolls-Royce

PAGE 229

Word Pyramid

T
(1) AT
(2) ANT
(3) ETNA
(4) AGENT
(5) EATING
(6) HEATING
(7) TEACHING

Answers

ANSWERS TO DO YOU KNOW?

p. 9: Tank
p. 15: 2
p. 16: A bird
p. 19: 1957 Ford Thunderbird
p. 22: Clarksville
p. 27: The Repeal of Prohibition
p. 29: Robert Louis Stevenson
p. 33: Daphne du Maurier
p. 43: Let the buyer beware
p. 47: Napoleon
p. 53: Switzerland
p. 59: James Cameron
p. 65: Orange
p. 68: Acid
p. 71: Switzerland
p. 73: Jackson
p. 76: 14; China borders Afghanistan, Bhutan, India, Kazakhstan, Kyrgyzstan, Laos, Mongolia, Myanmar (Burma), Nepal, North Korea, Pakistan, Russia, Tajikistan and Vietnam
p. 80: Dwight Eisenhower
p. 87: Cheddar
p. 93: Lake Superior
p. 102: Sparta
p. 105: It was the call, used on the Mississippi, meaning two fathoms
p. 107: Romagna water dog
p. 108: Herbert Hoover
p. 122: Tin
p. 125: Mexico
p. 129: Pessomancy
p. 131: Handel
p. 134: Scut
p. 137: The Wonderful Wizard of Oz
p. 138: A
p. 143: Kashmir goat
p. 144: 4 ½ inches

p. 149: Batman
p. 162: John Bunyan
p. 170: Bulgaria
p. 174: MG ZA Magnette
p. 175: 12
p. 178: 28
p. 179: Sorbonne
p. 186: Crane
p. 191: Marjorie Henderson Buell
p. 192: Portugal
p. 197: A fish
p. 200: Monica Seles
p. 207: Gruffi, Cubbi, Tummi, Zummi, Sunni and Grammi
p. 208: Melchior, Caspar and Balthazar
p. 216: She drowned
p. 219: A jenny
p. 225: The equator
p. 229: Wilma

ANSWERS TO TRIVIA

p. 15: Cheetah
p. 33: Jessie Owens
p. 59: John Wayne
p. 84: Trumpet
p. 105: They cool the elephant's blood
p. 138: The Manhattan Project
p. 144: They are the highest mountains in their respective continents: North America, South America, Africa, Australia
p. 150: (Nick) Bottom
p. 162: Charles Babbage
p. 175: A temperature of 136°F in the shade has been recorded in Libya
p. 179: Mexico, Luxembourg
p. 192: The zenith

CREDITS

Cover photo credit:
ziviani/Shutterstock

Puzzle credits:
Sam Bellotto Jr.: 133, 136, 160, 165, 181, 184, 196
David Bodycombe: 70, 145, 150, 172, 221
Guy Campbell and Paul Moran: 18, 96-97, 158–159
Peter Frank: Binairo, Kakuro, Number Cluster, Sudoku, Word Searches, Word Sudoku
Don Law: 52
John McCarthy: 31, 63, 154
Peggy O'Shea: 78
Karen Peterson: 113, 147
Emily Cox & Henry Rathvon: 23, 62, 109, 171
Ken Russell and Philip Carter: 194–195
John M. Samson: 11, 28, 45, 46, 72, 77, 116, 127, 142, 168, 173, 190, 201, 204, 227
Michele Sayer: 14, 17, 20, 34, 37, 86, 95, 110
Mary-Liz Shaw: 32, 104, 128, 189
Debra Steilen: 83
Thinks.com Ltd: 198–199
Tim Wagner: 58, 92
Cindy Wheeler: 49, 66, 98, 103, 119, 130
Kelly Whitt: 8, 25, 40, 55, 69, 89, 106, 124, 139, 148, 151, 157, 176, 193, 209, 212, 217, 220